# THE TRIUMPH
## OF
# THE TREE

*by*

JOHN STEWART COLLIS

LONDON  1951

THE
COUNTRY BOOK CLUB

*This*
*COUNTRY BOOK CLUB EDITION*
*was produced in 1951 for sale to its members only by The*
*Country Book Club Ltd at 38, William IV Street, London,*
*W.C.2., and at Letchworth Garden City, Hertfordshire, from*
*either of which addresses full particulars may be obtained.*
*The book is set in 12 point Baskerville type one point leaded,*
*and has been reprinted at the Alden Press, Oxford. It was*
*first published by Jonathan Cape Ltd.*

# CONTENTS

# CONTENTS

PART THREE

## THE TRANSITION

PART FOUR

## THE REVENGES OF NATURE

I THE GOVERNMENT OF NATURE AND
THE MINISTRY OF TREES

II MAN AND THE ORDER OF NATURE —
THE OLD WORLD

# CONTENTS

PART FIVE

# CONCLUSION

# ARGUMENT

WE were nursed into life by trees. It is to trees that we owe the development of a physiology which made Man possible — that is to say, made conceptual thought possible. Those fundamental facts should be sufficient to explain the intimate quality of man's relationship with trees. There is a still more practical side to the connection. Trees are necessary to our existence because they are the chief guardians of the soil, keeping it stable and watered. In the very ancient past, trees were thought to be spirits or the habitation of spirits, both good and evil, and finally were conceived as simply deities who were the guardians of fertility. This climate of thought lasted for some centuries in every country and led to a very widespread worship of trees and to an equally widespread fear of injuring them. We call it the Era of Mythology. This way of thinking gradually broke up and we entered the Era of Economics when trees and everything else were valued in cash. At the height of this economic era the application of science showed how swiftly and completely men could make use of trees in particular and nature in general. We have just reached the end of that period, having found that such an attitude has brought us to the edge of disaster. We are about to enter what might be called the last act of the drama, when science now discovers precisely in what way trees really are the guardians of fertility after all. This will be the Era of Ecology — the science of achieving an equilibrium with the environment. Thus having come full circle, we are back at the beginning again. But is it too late to make a fresh start? The world is not what it was at the beginning of the story.

## ARGUMENT

Half the wealth has gone. Even so, we *could* save the situation. But are we sufficiently alarmed to mend our ways? Do not too many people think, on the contrary, that we have done so extremely well that we can now actually look forward to entering an era when we will experience freedom from fear and freedom from want? But it is unlikely that we will experience much freedom from want until we have restored our capacity to fear the responses of nature.

PART ONE

IN THE FORESTS OF THE NIGHT

TO make our way back to the beginning of trees we must cross the boundless empires of Time, driving on over the geological eras, unfolding and still unfolding the manuscripts of stone, passing beyond the Quaternary and the Tertiary page, beyond the Cretaceous and the Jurassic, beyond the Triassic and the Permian, until we come to the measures of Carbon.

It is not easy to do this. The sheer length of time blurs our conceptions. When we face the eons and behold their sculpture our minds become dazed and we feel hopelessly separated from the early scenes. We make an error here, I think. Time is real enough; the carvings of its knife are proof of that; but we over-estimate the importance of distance. We allow it to make things unreal: even friends in a far country are only half-alive for us. But that which is far away, in space or in time, is just as real as that which is close at hand — and not nearly so unfamiliar as we sometimes think. Happily we can overcome this error and disperse this mist. For example, if we stand on the Scottish Highlands we can actually get a very good idea of what the earth was like long before even the Carboniferous Age, before the Devonian, the Silurian, or the Ordovician, before even the Cambrian. From those Highlands we can actually *see* the pre-Cambrian Age, we can stand upon the first rocks, the Lewislan Gneiss. Gazing upon the dark unhuman peaks where no flowers grow and no bird sings, we throw off the weight of time-distance and see what could have been seen five hundred million years ago. Certainly we can say without exaggeration if we gaze upon the rocks and forget the verdant valleys, that the spectacle which we see as we stand upon those desolate hills is much the same, and perhaps in parts actually the same, as what could have been seen at the beginning of earth's race when the mountains had been moved above the waters.

And if we wish to attend at the very beginning of vegetation we need not close our eyes and try to imagine the first clothing of the rocks when all the earth was bare. We can still watch the formation of the first plants. If we take a piece of bread and leave it exposed for a day or two it will become hoary with the grey stalks and powdery fructification of the mildew and the mould; if we throw a clean boulder into the glen beside its river it will soon be clothed with the first mercy of the moss; if we dam up water and make a stagnant pool the liquid mirror will not long serve to reflect the face of Narcissus, for it will soon become as green as a lawn with the growth of confervae which in time will choke up the whole and turn it into a bog; if we destroy our cities and cast down our towers they will be covered soon or late by these humble workers of the dawn. Thus they toiled in the dawn of life. They toil today, we see them do it — but then they were all that could be seen of verdure. Then they grew flesh upon the stony skeleton of earth. Then they wove the tapestries of the hills. Then they were the highest forms of organic existence, the first step forward in the flowering; they were the kings of life, and as they spread their royal mantle over all the earth they laid the foundation for the kingdoms of the world.

## § II THE PRIMEVAL FERNS

IT is likely that as soon as they began to advance at all they advanced swiftly, these moulds and mosses, lichens and algae, fungi and other cryptogamia. First a sort of slime no thicker than paint, gathering through the years in depth and texture and richness, laying a floor for tufty plants and at last a foundation for the first pedestals, the first *stalks*.

These last grew ever thicker and higher into forests of fern. Studying their print in the library of the rocks we are able to grasp the magnitude of their multiplication, their rank luxuriance, and the huge dimensions of their territory. In the library, one whole volume — vol. VI of the Series, coming between the Devonian and the Cambrian — is devoted to these plants, an era called the Carboniferous, calculated as three hundred million years ago, and as lasting for uncertain millions of years. This chapter in the history of the world, according to some authorities, saw this vegetation spread over the whole earth, from Melville Island in the extreme north to the Islands of the Antarctic Ocean in the extreme south.

Again we can see what was there to some extent by looking at their descendants here. We know what bracken looks like when fully grown — a miniature forest. Then that scarce penetrable phalanx of reeds and bracken attained the height of forest trees in our day — as if the horse-tails of our bogs were magnified sixty or a hundred times, as if our reeds, mosses and ferns had sprung up as giants. Larger still were the various kinds of tree-ferns, the Lepidodendrons and Sigillaria, called club-mosses, though they much more resembled palms and cycads. Their stems were ribbed and fluted like Gothic columns, and they grew leaves thickly, tier upon tier, gradually shedding the lowest. And mingled with them were some genuine trees, conifers such as we might recognize today — the first real trees to appear on earth. They were not proportionally large as were the ferns compared with our growths, not giants to our dwarfs, but normal.

These forests grew in very swampy soil if we can call it soil at all, with a carpet of fallen leaves, spore-dust, prostrate stems, mosses, and liverworts at their feet. It would have made squelchy sinking ground for any creature to tread upon who might wish to roam there or penetrate into the mystery of the measureless bogs and stems which then made up the landscape of the earth. No creatures did attempt this, for none existed. At least no air-breathing animals at first. There were plenty of water-breathing animals. Motor existence had advanced well beyond its earliest forms in the marine world. Some had run their race, giving way to others. The sun was sinking upon the kingdom of the trilobites, the horse-shoe crabs, and the eurypterids, while lobsters, hermit crabs, and true crabs took the stage, and scorpions, with twelve eyes disposed in a circle, entered the scene. But the air was not yet breathable. It had four times the amount of carbon as in the whole of the atmosphere today. The tree-ferns, in their enormous abundance, purified the air.

These tree-ferns, writes Fabre, 'constituted the greater part of the gloomy forests that were never enlivened by the songs of birds, nor resounded to the trample of the quadruped. As yet the dry land had no inhabitants. The atmosphere must have been unbreathable, for it contained, in suspension, in the shape of poisonous gas, the enormous amount of carbon which has since become coal. But the Tree-ferns, like other plants of their day, set to work in order to cleanse it and to render the solid earth habitable. They subtracted the world's carbon from the air, storing it in their leaves and stems; then falling into decay they made room for others, and these yet again for others, which unremittingly pursued, in the silence of the woods, their noble work of atmospheric salubrity. The purification of the atmosphere was at last accomplished, and the Tree-ferns died. Their remains, buried underground, have in course of time become coal measures, in which leaves and stems, wonderfully preserved as to form, are today to be found in abundance, and record, in their archives, the history of this ancient vegetation, which has given us an atmosphere that we can breathe, and has stored up for us in the bowels of the earth those strata of coal which are the wealth of nations'.

The appalling silence, from day to day and from year to year and from century to century, must indeed have been savage. Could we stand in such an atmosphere for a few minutes it would fall upon us with the oppression of impending calamity. Better far, we would feel, to hear the wild cries of pain that are the price of life, the shrieks and howls that answer the gift of air. We do not know for how long the unspeakable sadness of that silence bent over the flowerless, beeless seas of green, but the air must have been breathable for some centuries at the close of the Carboniferous Age, for the existence of many insects is established in the archives of stone. Here the spiders began to set up their everlasting line; the leaf-eating worms appeared in company with bugs, fireflies, lice, snails, centipedes, crickets, and cockroaches, while the flight of dragonflies, with a wingspread of twenty-eight inches, is vouched for by the photographers of clay. And gradually the Labyrinthodonts, precursors of the Dinosaurs, ancestral newts, whose long bodies were protected by an armour of plates like the tiles on a roof, emerged from the water and developed lungs. They have left us their footprints in the sand. They took a walk, three hundred million years ago — and we, today, know all about it!

How did these forests come to write their story in rock and to measure their weight in coal? 'Falling into decay they made room for others, and then yet again for others.' They did that, and they did more. They sank. At intervals they were overwhelmed by flood, and the land surface of forest disappeared. In due course sediment settled upon that submerged vegetation until it appeared above water again and served as the basis for a new forest. (That is one school of geological theory; another is that the submerged land was pressed upwards from time to time by forces below.) Whichever it was, the process was repeated. It was repeated numerous times. In Nova Scotia up to a hundred forests were buried, one above the other, with the roots of trees found still in their original positions, and with some of the trunks still standing erect; while at Essen the rocks reveal to us that *one hundred and forty-five separate forests*, each a land-surface on its own, were lowered down one on top of the other.

Thus, after drinking the sunshine these forests went down into the bowels of the earth to a depth sometimes equal to the height of Mont Blanc. And then, by cause of the terrific weight upon them, by the temperature, and by the pressure of the enormously patient, unbreakable and unbending tool of Time, they were squashed into pulp and hardened into rock. We call it coal. A bed one yard thick takes a thousand years to make — thus three million years were necessary to produce the South Wales field.

We take a piece of it in our hands, a black stone. It is carbon, it is sunshine shaped into a solid. It is a piece of the sun itself we hold, the blazing ball itself turned into the dirty darkness of that rock. It may be very cold, freezing to the touch on a winter's day; yet still it is the ancient furnace that we finger, it is heat made cold, a frozen burning beam. We do not doubt this for a moment. We know how to change it back, how make it into fire again. We put a piece of its own element in touch with it — its own essence, flame — and in a few minutes the box flies open and the trebly millioned years imprisoned sun streams out, and the ransomed rays that fell upon the ferns fall on us today.

All the plants of those forests were not ferns. Some of them, as already mentioned, were conifers such as we might recognize today — the great group of Gymnosperms. Thus here, in these carboniferous vistas, is the cradle; here the first nursery of trees. In these glades was matured the idea of not falling down.

Nature advances by process of big new ideas. Fall down and get up again — that was the old idea. Get up by virtue of seeds thrown down. Most vegetation still does this. The building of most plants collapses utterly after a season, and a new representative has to be set up. Then the great New Idea — to have stalks that would not wilt, to have stems that would not die, to set up columns that would outlast pedestals of stone! Thus trees. We can see the unfolding of the idea among the ferns. A tree-fern shows us the beginning. Having set up a pedestal for its fronds, the fern seems to have said one day — Why not start from here next time, instead of from the ground? A good idea, but how carry it out? If they were to have pedestals which would remain fresh and also be equal to the burden of supporting a growing capital, then certain novel architectural devices must be employed. In due course they were devised, and anyone in London who is prepared to go as far as Kew Gardens can see what could have been seen in those early days — ferns starting to set up their pedestals, and ferns with pedestals already established. Thus arrived the club-mosses, the sigillaria, the palms. And once the New Idea had been liberated and exhibited in visible form in the outer world, it was taken up and improved upon by other species, the first of which were conifers. When we hear the wind blowing through the pine trees, the least imaginative of us is stirred; we are carried back into the depths of Time when that melancholy moan was sounded long before the trampling of any feet.

§ IV THE LAPSE OF AGES AND THE YEAST
OF CREATION

THE scroll of Time unrolled. Calculating the incalculable, and endeavouring to measure our minds against the crushing milestones, we name the period that followed the Mesozoic, and count it as two hundred million years duration, ending some eighty million years ago. Once we grasp the fact that Time is so formidable, so utterly outside our ordinary conceptions, we can then see it as a concrete thing, rather like a chisel or a knife, at work upon the surface of the world, changing the shapes beyond recognition. The Palaeozoic and Azoic periods that preceded the Mesozoic are said now to claim about fourteen hundred million years. If we can face the impact of that Force we can accept without surprise the advance in organization as exemplified for instance between the slime-mould which parted company with some of its own members when meeting obstruction and later reassembled them (the parts being hardly more than jelly), and the gigantosaurus which exhibited a body a hundred feet long. Given that commodity, Time, in unlimited abundance, the creative force of life could do what it liked. The eye that could pass in review the periods that followed the earliest forests would behold the emergence into the now purified air, life, no longer stationary like trees, but moving about freely on never less than four and not more than four hundred supports or legs. Beneath the waters many other animals could have been seen at this time and well before it; but now they rose from the deep and in different shapes took to the air and the land. We have some of them with us to this day such as the tortoise, the crocodile and the lizard. The interesting thing is that at this early period in the history of animals the largest organizations appeared. The Dinosaurs are so far the top size in animals. That limit was never surpassed. And, as everyone knows, they did not do so well as the smaller animals, and they perished utterly. Perhaps their eggs were eaten by the smaller animals. But there is no great mystery: they could not possibly have survived a severe climatic change. They were succeeded by creatures who did a new thing.

Another New Idea. Animals evolved who gave up creating their young by laying them on the earth packed in a hard o or oval. They kept these oes or ovals inside themselves and presently delivered their young ready-hatched. And when they were hatched the mothers took an interest in them and gave them milk. These mammals, as we call them, set in motion a form of life never since abandoned by succeeding generations. From that time thousands of new forms became possible and life multiplied in such staggering variety that it looks as if variation is boundless and life as much a unity as water.

The great hammer strokes of Time continued to fall

upon the flora and fauna, and upon the appearance of the earth itself. Continents rose from the deep and sank again. The earth we know today, was not. Our Africas, Americas, Australias, Indias had no place, they were more and they were less. The vast Gwondaland that today we see no sight of, for a brief space of a few million years lay exposed to the sun where leagues of waves wash now. Lowlands became highlands and highlands were cast down. Endless eras lapsed. The fingers traced upon the stones are silent in relation to huge gaps of time; but we do know that during all this time, while life spread out more and more into ever new formations, while the creature about the size of a fox changed into what we call a horse, while the giraffe pushed up that neck and the elephant unrolled that trunk and so on, forests, ever increasing in strength, dominated the lowlands of the world. Not everywhere perhaps; but the amount of unbroken forest stuns the imagination, it appals the mind. Picture the space of an Atlantic Ocean all trees. Some of the forests cannot have been less than that — land oceans of leaf as seen from above.

And down below, under the surface of that leaf-ocean, what went on? There boiled the cauldron of life. There swarmed the yeast of creation. In those depths were prepared the fiercest and furthest forms issuing from the womb of the mighty mother. The silence of the carboniferous days was broken by the snarls coming from carnivorous jaws, by the clamour of growing life, by the moan and bitter burden of being born. We need not seek in imagination that dark backward and abysm of time to conjure the scene: it can still be watched in certain parts of the world, such as in the Bolivian jungles. There the traveller can still behold the frightful ferment of primary creation. 'I felt carried back twenty million of years to the primeval world', wrote Arthur Heye after having made an expedition to a pool in the Brazilian jungle. Speaking of the atmosphere at night, he says: 'Between the trees the turbid water was rippling gently beneath the fiery red of the blazing moon; the melancholy call of birds sounded in the gloaming, an almost inaudible rustle of wind went whispering through leaf and reed. But then the water was stirred with weird motion: a gurgling, splashing and rustling, an ever wilder spattering and plashing. The whole of the dead water was heaving with invisible life. And gradually I began to understand what life this was — and my hair stood on end. Those were crocodiles. The whole pool seemed to consist only of crocodiles! And now at night the reptiles were apparently falling upon each other; a continuous hollow bawl and roar arose from the centre of the pool; a furious lashing of tails, a loud rattling of jaws, a foaming bubbling of the water; and over the crest of the surging waves flashed the dusky red reflexes of the spectral moon.' He stood at a narrow branch of the water and saw no less than five hundred crocodiles pass by: they must have lain one on top of the other in the lagoon like packed herrings. It was the very yeast of creation: 'This is what the nights of the Jurassic sea must have been like, when the fights of the ichthyosaurians were raging amidst the vapours of carbonic acid clouds, and the lurid light of the still fiery moon gleamed down upon the scene.'

Again, the Spanish writer, José Eustasio Rivera, in *La Voragine*, speaks of the jungle with the same sense of early days — the overwhelming battle to come into existence and to remain in it, the destruction and renewal, the scent of death, and the ferment of procreation. 'Here dwell the responses of bloated toads; here

23

are the pent waters round rotting reeds. The aphrodisiac parasite is the master here, strewing the earth with dead bees; here is the varied wealth of obscene flowers contracting like sexual organs, whose sticky odour inebriates like a drug; here is the malignant liana whose downy beard blinds the animals; and the pringamosa which enflames the skin.' And his description of the night scenes would surely stand for the unwitnessed spectacles of the primal years when the law was writ large that all coming into existence is fraught with filth and horror. What the philosophy of pure Spirit, as Keyserling put it, would banish to the very depths of Hell, is the earthly womb of all life. 'In the night unknown voices, phantasmagoric lights, funereal silence. Death passes on its way and gives life. There is the sound of fruit crashing down with the promise of seed as it bursts; the fall of the leaf filling the mountain recesses with vague sighs, the offering of itself as dung to the parent tree; the crunching of jaws eating for fear of being eaten; the squealing of the disturbed, the moans of the dying, the belching of creatures easing themselves. And when the burning dawn reveals the tragic splendour above mountain peaks, the tumult of the surviving sets in: the cooing of doves, the grunting of boars, the grotesque laughter of monkeys.'

§V TREES THE PREREQUISITE OF CONCEPTUAL
THOUGHT AND THE BIRTH OF MAN

WE have got as far as monkeys. Sooner or later amongst the new Appearances in the forest there rose the monkeys. They did a new thing.

Hitherto there had been the earth-bound animals with legs and the air-borne animals with wings. The monkeys left the ground without riding the air. They made the trees their habitation. In due course this promoted the development of something new in the history of all the creations. The monkeys started with four legs in the ordinary manner. Gradually they changed their two front legs into something else — they created *arms*. And while they discarded front legs for the new things called arms, they also substituted something else for the front feet — they made *hands*.

The most important thing which ever happened in the forest was the creation of the HAND.

The Arm, the Hand, the Finger, the Thumb: consider the destinies that lay enfolded there!

This brings us to man.

For the next great event was the appearance of the first men. How did they come? We all know the popular theory about this. When the lemurs or apes or monkeys had after thousands of years so altered their bodies as to stand upright on two legs and to possess real arms and hands — then the First man appeared. Presumably he looked just like the Last ape of that line — with an infinitesimal difference which multiplied and multiplied until real men such as we would recognize today in a primitive community became common, and in their turn increased.

Such is the famous story of man's evolution from the animals. It has not yet been determined whether we really stemmed from the apes, or whether we had a stem of our own from which the apes degenerated. It is unlikely that any Missing Link could clear this up. And the main mystery does not seem subject to solution. When we talk about evolution we are concerned with two things, one easy and the other difficult. It is easy to grasp and accept the main idea of evolution — that of an endless variety of species forming by the clash of growth with circumstance. It is distinctly queer that one of the animals should have ceased to be an animal and become something else. Why did only man do what man did? All the other animals went on being animals for thousands of years and seem likely to continue to do so. What is the difference between being an animal and being a man? It lies in the fact that man possesses conceptual thought and the specific instrument that goes with it — language. How is it that no other animal has broken into conception and speech? The answer is perhaps given in Dr. Julian Huxley's very illuminating essay, *The Uniqueness of Man*, by his detailed assertion that *only* the physiology of the Primates (lemurs, apes, monkeys) could promote the evolution of conceptual thought. That is, one animal did not cease to be an animal, but became an animal with conceptual thought. Still, we are left wondering why, if this is so, no monkeys are ever found now slowly becoming men. And if monkeys are de-evolutionary types of men, why do they not show signs of real speech?

Whatever the solution may be, man did arrive. And we must note the responsibility of trees in this matter. The existence of trees was a prerequisite of conceptual thought. It was the tree that gave the hand to life. It was the tree that promoted the upright posture. It was the tree that made sight dominant over smell. Thus it was the tree that 'laid the foundation both for the fuller definition of objects by conceptual thought and for the fuller control of them by tools and machines'.[1]

Must we not say that it was the tree that gave man to life? Anyway, it was under the auspices of those

[1] *The Uniqueness of Man.*

ancient boughs that he appeared. And having appeared, he was destined to interfere with the Order of Nature. The very forests were doomed.

We are accustomed to think of nature and man as the norm. But man has only been at work for a million years out of the two hundred million (if that is the figure). During all those years nature developed according to the terrifying Order which we can still see. Had it continued thus for the last million years, imagine the world today. Consider a journey through it. Not a man, not a city, not a machine, not a road: an almost universal forest broken here and there by bare mountain peaks and the great waters. Think of the surging life breaking ceaselessly like waves upon the shore and as ceaselessly dragged screaming back into the jaws of death: the untamed beauty of it all — unseen, unfeared, unpraised. Then man enters. He looks like any other organized piece of nature. Will not the world of life go on just as it has always done? But he soon showed that he was utterly different from *all* the other stationary and motor organisms on earth. His eyes communicated something to his mind which the eyes of the other creatures did not communicate. He saw the world objectively. He became a spectator — something quite new. We call it consciousness. The other animals had eyes, ears, hearts and brains, but not this, and no tendency to evolve this.

That is the curious thing. It holds most interest for us today. In the last century it was man's similarity to animals, his kinship with them, his ascent from them, that came as a revelation. Now that we have grasped the reality of evolution one way or another, it is no longer our likeness to the animals that interests us and stirs us most deeply: it is our unlikeness to them, our singular gift of consciousness that has separated us from the flow of nature. Man alone stood back and looked at the world. He stooped down and picked up pieces of it, and used those pieces — even fire. The centuries roll on and yet no other creature is ever seen using a tool or lighting a fire! That wonderful Hand, given us by the tree, began to change the appearance of the world. Up till then life was in the hands of God: now man became one of the hands of God — nay, God was delivered into the hands of men.

§ VI MAN'S CRADLE IN THE FORESTS

WE will probably never know much about the earliest dates of man's existence. Some anthropologists speak of his arrival as occurring 'after the first Ice Age'. This is very difficult to believe. The line of his descent (or ascent) was obviously arboreal. His existence pre-supposes the existence of forests, and forests pre-suppose anything but an ice age. It is much more likely that man appeared before the first Ice Age and then taking to caves survived into the next warm period. The geologists give us four such cold periods. It is extremely hard to visualize them. These ages are spoken of as if something like a world-wide glacier slowly expanded over the earth. At the same time we hear of men living in caves and going out to hunt a variety of animals, and after hunting sitting by fires. Where did they get the fuel? Where were those animals and how did they exist if it was an ice age? We must suppose that these ice ages were not so severe as they are made out to be.

Happily this is not my concern. It is my privilege to unwind the ball of Time until we come to primitive man in the primeval forests slowly working his way into consciousness. He began, we began, amongst trees. Our story began when the earth's surface consisted chiefly of water and wood. The oceans! the forests! — the very words stir us still. They carry us back into the wondrous depths of the dawn, echoing and re-echoing our first fearful fumblings in the dark.

We began amongst trees. Can we imagine now what it was like living in the days of that beginning? We can have some idea; for though the corrosions of Time do carve incredible changes on the creatures and the landscapes of the earth, there are some things which repeat themselves so closely as seeming to ignore the passage of centuries. Amongst such we may consider the tropical forests of today. If we know something of them we can imagine something of the environment of our earliest ancestors, and therefore something of their feelings.

They came into the first glimmerings of consciousness in the forests. That was their world, all they saw, all they knew — a world of trees. If ever they were in a position to see the tops of the trees they would see a green prairie stretching out oceanically to the ringed horizon. From below, the forest could be seen as a kind of unlimited table with tree-trunks for legs. To this day many animals inhabit these table-tops as if they were the earth below. Squirrels and sloths, tree-porcupines and tree-ant-eaters, tree-frogs and toads, not to mention a variety of birds, inhabit the forest-roofs without necessarily ever descending to the ground — so that even tadpoles are born in the high leaves that have gathered water, and there, in the arboreal ponds, suffer the stages of metamorphosis. We might truly call these surfaces *table-lands* in which the creatures live: not flying in air, not swimming in water, not stationed on soil or rock — but slung between heaven and earth.

Such a canopy above meant much gloom and darkness below. And it was there that men must have dwelt in forest clearings. Dig a hole in the Atlantic Ocean; make a clearing in the water, and tent yourself down there in that cliffed-in place — and you probably would not feel more overwhelmed by the walls of water than in the old days when we lived at the bottom of the seas of trees.

When today we enter the tropical forests we do so with perhaps a million years' consciousness of the world behind us. And whether we live in it as natives or visit it as travellers, we are still subdued by it. It is not easy for a modern European to grasp what it means to dwell in a primeval forest. As I write these lines I sit within the shade of an English wood. I hear the hum of wasps and bees, and the call of birds, and in the distance the voices of children (whose cries always echo far where there are trees). It is not wholly quiet nor silent. Yet quietness is here, and silence. Nature's holy nuns surround me in the congregation of their convent. Here I am set in the midst of liberty and peace. In these gentle climes trees are friends to us, and in their presence, amidst the calm of their cathedral aisles, we are prone to meditate upon the blessedness of life.

It is not so in the great forests of the world. There we will not find benediction. The silence is as terrifying as the noise. The oceans of unvoyaged verdure, the brutal entanglement of parasitic lianas that rope with wild riggings the branches of the endless trees, make a scene that soon tames and humbles down the hardest man. The spells of silence, silence us — nay, subdue us utterly by sense of the violence pent up in that stillness. Then it explodes. It cracks across. Thunder goes off like a cannon behind our ears. Earth's foundations falter. Rain and hail fall as if an army from above were hurling down stones and buckets of water. Fiery bolts of metal crash like bombs. The darkness is figured by screens and serpents of white fire. This is the END we cry. It is finished. All is lost. The world reels back now to its beginnings. Then the tempest stops as suddenly as it began, and the dawn breaks upon an earth still fresh and strong, glinting in the rays of the rising sun. Our fear is cast aside and our hearts expand in joyfulness and praise.

Thus even today we know Fear in the forests. Otherwise we seldom know it. A thunderstorm is good fun, we rejoice in it. The wilder it is the better, we are glad to see nature violent and scathing. But we have lost that fear which is a clutch at the heart, and in order to achieve it we must resort to the thunder of oncoming enemy aeroplanes. And now some people are advocating freedom from fear. That might be all right from a physical point of view, but how about the metaphysical? In the Middle Ages three monks came to Father Sisoes and complained that they were continually pursued by three things: fear of the river of fire, of the worm which dies not and of the outer darkness. When the Saint made no reply they were greatly distressed. Finally he said: 'My brothers, I envy you. As long as such thoughts live in your souls it will be impossible for you to commit a sin.' We must not forget that religion unfolds from the womb of fear. The most intense form of religion is superstition. The most superstitious man is the most religious of all religious men — for he is most in touch with, most sensitive to the *numinous*, the Other, the invisibilities, the god-forces. It is not at all a good thing to be too religious, for then you will far too often be foolish and frantic: but I do not know how it will be proved that to have no respect for the elemental powers, even while using them to blow yourself up, is to be wiser and more profound.

Let us beat our way back across the deserts of Time and think of man coming into consciousness as he dwelt in the deep forests of that ancient day.

## § VII   THE ROOTS OF MYTHOLOGY

'COMING into consciousness.' A phrase. We write it down. We take it as thought and pass on. But what's the good? Let us think what we are saying. To come into consciousness: can we, who are in consciousness, imagine this event which changed the history of practically all life on earth except some insects, and which altered the top surface of most of the world?[1] The animal walked along, it still walks along, submerged in the stream of life in which it moves, though it is not like a drifting piece of wood, since it has an engine of its own and is conscious of itself. But it is without consciousness of the world as something it can look at objectively. How do I know this, seeing that I am not an animal and have never looked out at the world from behind the pale windows of that kingdom? Because if it had conceptions we would soon know it. I look at the sun rising. An animal looks at the sun rising. It sees the same thing. But it cannot see it as the sun rising. It cannot see it as something to be thought about and named. No animal can do this nor seems ever likely to do so however long its race survives or however much it may evolve — though, unless our stem is a unique growth, one animal once did so.

Anyway, the thing happened. One creature broke away from the determined life, drew back, looked on, and perceived the world as something to be conceived.

[1] Every anthropologist will realize that here I telescope the process: some thousands of years may well have passed before man's consciousness became differentiated materially from the animals, and became *self-consciousness*.

Can we imagine now what it felt like to be the New creature emerging into this awareness? We know what he felt like physically: the movements of the legs, the stomach, the throat, we know what it felt like to be him in that way. Very well; now let us take the eye. He saw out of it just as we do. But what did he see? Supposing for the sake of argument that the change was sudden, what was the difference between the last day when he was an ape and the first day when he was a man? Here we cannot think from experience. We do not remember. All we can say is that on that last day objects must have stood or moved in front of his eyes unidentified as objects, though they might react upon his senses in terms of fear or hunger. On that first day there was a communication exchanged between his eye and his brain, and an object was picked out, *separated*, and perceived as an object in itself. It is a pity we do not know the first word he spoke when he broke into speech. It must have been a sound that meant a question. By asking that question and picking out that object he took the first step in separating himself from the flow of phenomena.

Having become aware of the world, he at once set to work to separate everything in it, to sort out one thing from another. He did this by *naming* them. He began giving names to things, and today we will not find anything in the world that has not been given a name; or, if such a thing is found it is regarded as a great discovery. He began to give names to men themselves, so that today it is impossible to find a person without a name. *What is his name?* we ask, assuming that he has a name as certainly as he has a head or hand. The gulf between ourselves and the other creatures is seen most clearly in matters such as this. They live unnamed amongst each other — such is their lack of conception. Think of a

formicary of ants, each ant with a name: impossible! —
even amongst monkeys impossible.

Having become aware of objects and begun to name
them, this Earliest Man became aware of something else.
It is a remarkable fact that no sooner had he looked
closely at the phenomena of nature than he began to
concern himself with, not the visible object in front of
him which he could clearly see, but with an invisible
object which he could not see at all. He looked at the
trees, the rocks, the rivers, the animals, and having
looked at them he at once began to talk about something
*in them* which he had never seen and never heard of.
This thing inside the objective appearance was called a
god. No one forced man at this time to think about
gods, there was no tradition imposing it upon him — and
yet his first thoughts seem to have turned towards a
Thing behind the thing, a Force behind or within the
appearance. Thus *worship* — the very thought of which
in connection with any animal seems ludicrous.

All this is such an old story and has been gone over
so often by anthropologists, this evolution into worship
and birth of priesthood, that we tend to regard it all as
quite natural. After the event things always seem
natural and obvious. But before the event? One
wonders how many of the heavy-weight anthropologists
could ever have prophesied the birth of worship as an
early result of the birth of consciousness.

To sum up: suddenly (if in fact slowly) the circle was
broken, and certain creatures, that is to say ourselves,
achieved the power to look at the world with surprise
and question. The motion of the wind, the utter transformation of trees in season, the coming and the going
of the sun, the fall of water, were observed as strange
things. The dawning mind began to ask questions.

Surrounded on all sides by the extraordinary nature of the ordinary, faced with the strange object of a TREE, and having fixed it down with a Name, what did we do? Did we then look at it calmly and examine it? No! — that is the scientific spirit, something not to be born for many centuries. We immediately ceased to look at it, to see what was there. We saw what was not there. We obscured its existence with an orgy of fancies.[1] We saw beings that did not exist, we heard voices that spoke not, we bowed down before innumerable spirits whom we named. This remarkable attitude of mind has of course been dealt with by specialists the world over. It is now called Mythology and has been examined, docketed, labelled, categorized, and shelved. Let me take it down from the shelf — in so far as it touches trees — and place it before you as something which once we really did experience.

[1] Yet behind the fancies was the intuition of living unity that we call *animism* — which is far from fanciful.

# BIBLIOGRAPHY

BERRY, E. W., *Tree Ancestors*

CAMPBELL, D. H., *Structure and Development of Mosses and Ferns*

COULTER, T. M. and CHAMBERLAIN, C. J., *The Morphology of Gymnosperms*

DARWIN, CHARLES, *The Origin of Species*

FABRE, H., *The Wonder Book of Plant Life*

GATTI, COMMANDER, *Great Mother Forest*

GEIKIE, A., *Text Book of Geology*

HAVILAND, D., *Forest and Steppe*

HULL, E., *The Coal Fields of Great Britain*

KEYSERLING, H., *South American Meditations*

LYELL, C., *A Manual of Elementary Geology*

MACMILLAN, H., *The First Forms of Vegetation*

MILLER, H., *The Old Red Sandstone*

NICHOLSON, H. A., *The Ancient Life History of the World*

RECLUS, E., *The Earth*

REID, C., *Submerged Forests*

RIVERA, J. E., *La Voragine*

SCOTT, D. H., *Evolution of Plants*

SEWARD, A. C., *Geology*

STOPES, M., *Ancient Plants*

STOPES M. and WHEELER, R. V., *Monography on the Constitution of Coal*

TRUEMAN, A. E., *An Introduction to Geology*

WEBSTER SMITH, *The World in the Past*

WELLS, H. G., *The Outline of History*

WELLS and HUXLEY, *The Science of Life*

WILSON, J. H., *The Miraculous Birth of Language*

PART TWO

# THE MYTHOLOGY OF TREES

A CERTAIN trader in Africa living in a place wholly cut off from civilization was in the habit of sending a basket of food to a colleague who lived at some distance. A native who undertook to deliver it felt hungry one day during his journey and proceeded to eat a loaf and some eggs taken from the basket. When he delivered the basket the recipient glanced at a slip of paper in it and at once declared that the man had eaten those things. The native, amazed and alarmed at such divination, confessed and was beaten. But on another journey with the same basket he again felt hungry and again determined to have some of the food. But he was terrified of that slip of paper. It did not occur to him that the scratches on it had any meaning. To him that paper was obviously alive and had *told* the other man about his theft. It had seen what he did. This time he hid it out of sight while he helped himself, so that it could not possibly watch him. But when he reached the other end again the paper still told all. After this he made no further attempts to hoodwink it.

An episode of that kind does more than any hard effort of imagination on our part to help us conceive the frame of consciousness of the early human beings. That piece of paper had no eyes, no ears, no face, no arms or legs; yet to the native it was alive and could watch him and tell others what he had done. We all possess scientific minds in comparison. One is reminded of the Brazilian Indian who informed a missionary (known to Levy-Brühl) that he himself was a red parrot. In spite of what to us would seem convincing proof to the contrary the Indian continued to insist that he definitely was a red parrot. Nothing is more interesting in the history of human thought than how men of one generation are able to believe things which to men of another generation are out of the question. We learn not to be surprised at any belief.

The brief glance which I have already given at the early history of man and trees has taken us only to the time when he came to consciousness in the forests where he was cradled. There are no definite records of what he felt and saw, or thought he saw, in those early days; but if a primitive man today can think that a piece of paper is as alive as a human being, what must have been the effect of the mighty trees upon the first human inhabitants of the world! They must have seemed god-like creatures to be placated at all costs. We are without detail concerning those days. What wild imaginings, what frantic fears were theirs; what human sacrifice was made, what blood and tears were shed; what rejoicing in the spring-tide of the leafy waves — this in detail we can never know. We do know according to the records left by far later generations, together with contemporary anthropology, that the impression which trees once made must indeed have been unsurpassed by any other phenomena. For the wild worship went on and on almost up till modern times in some European places, while amongst those races which though living in the twentieth century have been left behind by Time, the data is very striking.

In any case it requires no great effort on our part to imagine in some degree what impression the quite ordinary things must have made in the beginning. When the wind howled it seemed as obvious to early intelligence that some Being made that noise as it is obvious to us

that the sound of a whip going through the air pre-
supposes someone holding the whip. The roar of
thunder came from an angry god as surely as to us the
roar of a lion proceeds from a lion's throat. I have
walked in woods so silent and secretive with hidden
waiting powers that I have almost felt as if I were in a
haunted house. Imagine the effect of untamed forests
upon minds unscored by knowledge. We have all seen
stunted ash trees look like witches; we have seen the
lichen-hoary wrecks of fallen trunks abandoned to the
reign of moss and mounted by strange shapes of fungi
take on a fearful aspect; we have seen many a still ghost
in the darkness of snowy nights on winter boughs; we
have seen mists clinging to the lower parts of trunks,
and later move and creep away like creatures of another
world, and as frightening in their silence as shades risen
from the gloomy pit of deepest Erebus; we have heard
voices echoing through woods and the cries of children
raised, though neither man nor child were there; we
have lost our way when far from home, while the forbidding boles betrayed us into futile gropings for our
goal. When the mind of man was first confronted with
these things in a far more fearful form, and when his
body was anything but safe from harms, and his days
were ringed and ruled by plans for sheer survival in the
midst of many foes, we can understand if only dimly
how his fancy ran away with him and he saw a thousand
things that were not there. He heard real sounds and
then conjured up their shapes before his eyes. He saw
gods and demons; he saw ogres, spirits, genii, and jinns;
he saw witches, goblins, and trolls; he saw nymphs and
gnomes, naiads and fauns, dryads and hamadryads; he
saw satyrs and centaurs, cyclops and silvani; he saw
fairies, elves, brownies, pixies, and leprechauns. He

peopled the woods with creatures who never existed. For, in all ages, there is no more untrustworthy person than the eye-witness.

§ II   SOME  TREE-DEMONS:  THE  GHOSTLY
HUNTSMAN

W H A T we do know for certain about the deification and devilization of trees is remarkable enough. From every part of the world details concerning that fear and that worship have come down to us.

The belief in forest demons and evil spirits reached its greatest development in Africa. The people were surrounded and thwarted by them at every turn. In every hollow, every cleft, every grove, every cave the spirits lurked; and wherever there was a scar, a disease, a broken branch — there was the work of spirits who must be propitiated by some offering. No man dared go alone at night through the forest. The Bongos and the Niam-Niams heard in the rustle of the foliage the conversation of demons conspiring against them; but if they laid hold of certain magic roots they could escape the influence of the evil spirits and at the same time learn a way to destroy their neighbours. Between the Niger and the Senegal grew a silk-cotton tree which was the abode of a spirit called Huntin who demanded sacrifices of fowls and of human beings, and as a devil could compete with Sasabonsum the demon who attacked wayfarers in the forest at night and ate them, and after his night of carnage sank beneath the ground having reddened the earth with the blood of his victims. The latter was very large and clothed in scarlet, and even those who escaped his clutches and reached home in safety, then expired. But he was always ready to assist anyone who wanted to become a witch, while his wife, Srahman, who was exceedingly tall and clothed in white (for her abode was in the white stem of the silk-cotton tree) was kinder to unhappy wayfarers, merely detaining them for some months while she taught them the secrets of the forests and the herbs.

Demons in one form or another cast their spell in all the forests of the world where men abode. In Russia the wood-demon called Ljeschi was partly of human form, with the horns, ears, and feet of a goat, his fingers being claws and his rough hair coloured green. He could assume what size he chose; in the woods as tall as the trees, in the fields no higher than grass: now like a man clothed in sheepskins, now a cyclops with only one eye. He could be seen in the storm springing from tree to tree, screeching and laughing, neighing, lowing and barking, and evidently bent upon misguiding the traveller and luring him into difficulties. In Arabia the dense untrodden thickets which fill the bottom of valleys were inhabited by jealous jinns who forbade cultivation, and if disturbed by would-be agriculturalists were seen to escape in the form of white serpents uttering doleful cries and pronouncing a curse upon their disturbers which brought about their death. In Persia the malignant demon, Siltim, haunted the forests in human form and spelt pain and injury to men wherever he appeared. In India certain spirits known as the Vanadevatâs dwelt in trees and revenged themselves upon anyone who cut them down, and a legend refers to the demons in Banyan trees who would wring the necks of all persons who approached their tree during the night, while almost equally dreaded were the Pishashas who hated anyone passing from one village to another and especially laid their curse upon pregnant women, who tried to propitiate them with articles of clothing or frighten them by carrying pieces of iron. In Burma and Siam the natives were afraid to cut down any trees lest they incurred wrath and suffered punishment: when the trees trembled they offered up prayers to the angry spirits, but they could find no means of escape from Hmin, the Ague Demon, who ranging at large through the forests violently shook all whom he met. In Japan the grotesque shapes of gnarled and time-scarred trunks were but the expression of malignant spirits who filled all woodmen with unspeakable dread, the most horrifying examples of which were the demons called Tengus who dwelt in the highest branches of lofty trees. With the body of a man, the head of a hawk, and the nose of a pelican; with claws instead of hands, and taloned feet on stilt-like clogs a foot high, they were born from eggs, and in their youth appalled the traveller by the magnitude of their wings and the ghastly hue of their feathers.

In many countries it was believed that a multitude of supernatural beings were ever on the watch to injure and slay all who entered the sad and lonely glades. In Malay no man dared enter the forest alone by night or day. Before advancing a step through the terrible trees a man would cry out, seeking to avert the demonic wrath by repeating the incantation as he went along —

> Peace unto ye all!
> I come as a friend, not as an enemy.
> I come to seek my living, not to make war.
> May no harm come to me, nor mine,
> To my wife, my children, or my home,
> Because I intend no harm, nor evil,
> I ask that I may come, and go, in peace.

And the further he went the more earnest became his

incantations. He feared these spirits as he feared the tiger and the lion. Often, under the impression that the voice of a brother was calling him, he went in the direction of the voice and was led further and further into the darkness of those verdant deeps until at last a person was seen. But that being was not human. He was a member of the Voice Folk who thereupon doomed their victim to become one of themselves, henceforth invisible to men while yet his voice could be heard eternally echoing in anguish from the confines of some complaining dim retreat.

It is remarkable with what clarity and detail the spirits were 'seen', and with what particularity the people sometimes dealt with them. The natives belonging to the district surrounding Gulvink Bay in British New Guinea saw in the mists which clung to the tops of high trees a spirit they called Narbrooi. He often drew away the soul of any human he fancied. If a man fell ill his companions thought his soul had been taken by Narbrooi. Therefore, one of his friends would go to one of those high trees, make a peculiar sound and light a cigar. When the smoke curled up from it Narbrooi would be kind enough to appear, looking young and elegant, and would intimate whether, on the receipt of suitable offerings, he would return the soul. It would then be conveyed in a straw bag back to the sufferer.

The particularity of human contact with tree-demons is curiously illustrated by the story of Oorangi, a native of Fiji amongst the ironwood trees, and the devil Vaotere. Oorangi on hearing that a huge ironwood tree would be much prized if he cut it down and exported the wood, attempted to carry this out with the help of four comrades. They found it possessed four great roots which they proceeded to cut. This task took some days, but each time on returning to their work they found the roots as intact as ever. Nevertheless by means of each man applying himself steadily to one root, the tree eventually fell. Two of them died on the way home. And when next day Oorangi returned with his two remaining men, they found the tree erect again, but blood-red in colour. On returning home the two survivors out of the four helpers also died. Soon afterwards Oorangi himself died. Then a stranger stepped forward, Ono, who came from the original land of the ironwoods and possessed an iron-wood spade of splendid properties. With this talisman Ono would do battle with the demon Vaotere. On reaching the tree he dug up the earth above all the roots. Day after day, unassisted, the mighty Ono pursued the roots in all their deviations over hill and valley, leaving the big ones but chopping off the numerous small ones and causing the chips to fly away in all directions under the blows of his wonderful spade. At last he had bared all the surface roots and now severed them at their extremities, so that the tree began to totter. The tap-root alone remained. Ono dug down until he had ex-posed it, and then with one final blow cut it off. This stroke caused the demon Vaotere to become visible and to display a visage as horrible in its pictorial effect as its mouth was frightful with gigantic teeth. It prepared to make an end of Ono. Here would it spill his soul. But it was not quick enough. With another blow of his spade Ono split the skull of the apollyon. Thereafter he examined the four great roots which were, indeed, the arms of Vaotere; and he then cut up the trunk which was the body of his victim. The chips from the small roots which had fallen over hill and dale grew up and origi-nated an ironwood forest — in which no Vaotere could now injure mankind.

Turn where we may we find devilish spirits of one sort
or another. In Australia the aborigines believed that
every thicket and grove was populated by evil spirits,
malicious devils who whispered from the Bush and
stooped from the trees with outstretched arms to seize
the traveller. Throughout the whole of Europe they
made a great impression. They were often clothed in
moss and their long locks floated behind them in the gale.
They announced their presence in the wind: they rode
the tempest. When they fought together they threw
rocks at each other and used as hand-weapons the uprooted trunks of pine trees. The wild tree-women of
the Tyrol were just as terrifying as these males: their
enormous bodies were covered with hair and bristles, and
their faces split across by a mouth that ran from ear to
ear. But perhaps they were not so typical as the Moss-
Women of Central Germany. It is easy to see their
origin. Grey and old-looking and hideously overgrown
with moss, they were trees walking — their feet like
knotty roots, their hair like lichen, their skin like maple-
rind ridged, furrowed, and scarred, and their flat
features like the open wound of a cut bough lapped over
by the renewing bark.

And in the New World we hear of similar reports as
from the Old. To the North American Indians the
oceans of forest land harboured the most abominable
tree-demons, one-eyed jointless fiends who ran swifter
than the black-tailed deer; and when mariners passed
by the wooded islands off the coast of Newfoundland they
were appalled by the shrieks of monsters engaged at the
celebration of hideous orgies in their infernal dens. In
the forests of Central America a bird-headed woman
whose personal beauty was only equalled by the divinity
of her voice, lured men towards her and then embraced

them with sentence of death. And at the mouth of the Amazon there was such an atmosphere of haunting ghosts and devils that the canoe-men attempted to propitiate them by hanging on the trees offerings of rags, shirts, bunches of fruit, and straw hats.

From many parts of the world came news of the madly riding and eternal Huntsman. We cannot call him a demon exactly, though at times he was shocking and frightful enough. He hunted eternally through the forest causing storms by the fury of his career. He was seen in Germany, Scandinavia, India, Malay, America and elsewhere. His existence was accounted for in many different ways. The most popular view held that he was a great huntsman who on his death-bed instead of paying heed to the exhortations of a priest with regard to his spiritual condition, cried out, 'The Lord may keep his Heaven so He leave me my hunting!' This prayer was granted with a vengeance. His desire became his doom. His pleasure was turned into everlasting punishment. From thenceforth he was dedicated to ceaseless chase. He must hunt until the Day of Judgment. When the storm raged in the forest he could be seen accompanied by his carriage, his horses, and his hounds madly pursuing his way. In Germany his approach was heralded by the long-toned hunting cries of the rider, together with the barking of the ghostly hounds, so that the affrighted travellers would throw themselves face downwards on the ground hoping that this chariot of the damned would pass them by. In Malay the Spectral Huntsman carried sickness and death as he ranged through the forests on his unending quest. Sometimes an owl flew in front of him, its weird noiselessness contrasting with the cry and the clatter of his coming, while other

48

birds of night were said to be his attendants. Sometimes he was seen by the Scandinavians rushing past on a white horse preceded by coal-black hounds, carrying his head under his left arm. In whatever country he appeared and with whatever panoply, he was always conceived of in this aspect of damnation; an exile from Heaven; clothed in the poetry of woe; doomed like Ahashurus the everlasting Jew to wander eternally across the world until the dawning of the Judgment Day.[1]

## §III THE GENTLE SPIRITS

MANY of the denizens of the woods were of a more amiable nature. Thus the spirit called Frau Wachholder was a friend to honest men and could be invoked to make thieves give up their booty. Since she was considered to be the genius of the juniper tree, those who had been robbed went to a juniper bush, bent one of its branches to the ground, and kept it down with a stone, meanwhile calling upon the thief, who then declared himself. Not less amiable was the sprite, Muma Padura, known to the Rumanians, who helped to find and rescue children who had lost their way in the woods. Others were to be pitied — such as the Woodwives. In Scandinavia they were conceived as young and beautiful at one moment, and old and ugly at another; and from some accounts, though lovely in front were hideous and hollow behind; and worse still, possessed a tail which they were anxious to conceal — highly symbolic creatures! They were generally thought of as small and were fair game for the Wild Huntsman, though they were safe from harm if they reached a tree with a cross on it.

[1] I know some people in Dorset who still hear him at midnight clattering past their house, stopping dead at the corner and disappearing.

They often approached women when baking and asked for a cake, or begged woodcutters to mend their little wheelbarrows. In recompense for food and assistance they changed wood chips to gold, or as in the case of the Dirne-weibls of Bavaria, they would display a basket of apples which turned into money. They loved human company and would weep if turned away. They were famous for weeping and wailing. Poor little things! They did not exist? Ah yes, they did and do — at least as truthful mirrors of the thoughts and yearnings, of the greed for riches, of the sorrow and the fear that sit enthroned within our hearts. Would'st know thyself? Then read mythology. No need for Jung or Freud to tell us more. That ghostly Huntsman on his mad march is not yet exorcized from our Faust-tormented souls. The external devils may have gone, but who save Christ could cleanse the demons from our own infernal dens?

In the same way we can appreciate the variety of lighter folk who were thought to inhabit the forests of the world. The fairies appeal to us still. There is something in us that loves to fancy what our ancestors thought they saw in the shape of tiny fairies, clothed in green, dancing hand in hand round trees in the moonlight. They lived in flowers and fed upon honey. It does not strike us as strange. When we read about Ariel we are not puzzled nor think it ridiculous, we accept it at once as if we were children. Nothing could be more fantastic or far-fetched than the idea that Prospero could open a pine tree and let Ariel get out. Yet we accept it easily just as we accept the fact that Sycorax by the help of her most potent ministers and in her most unmitigable rage did confine him there, within which rift he remained a dozen years venting his groans; and we are quite prepared to hear Prospero threaten to rend an oak and peg him in its knotty entrails till he has howled away twelve winters.

The fairies and elves were always thought of as tiny creatures dancing on the greensward, making merry, and ready to do some amiable service for human beings. Each country had its own type of fairy, and many people think that the English examples were the most delicately conceived. When Shakespeare came to confer immortality upon Fairy Mythology we realize how nothing could be more English, and less Germanic, say, than his Ariel and his Puck; and certainly there is nothing more English than Titania's bower which was 'A bank whereon the wild thyme blows, Where oxlips and the nodding violet grows'. Until quite recently there were peasants in Worcestershire who claimed to have been 'Poake-ledden', that is to say waylaid by a sprite they called Poake who led them into ditches and quagmires while he was heard laughing at their bewilderment. These Puck-like practical jokes were known in Devonshire as being 'Pixie-led', and under such influence men could not find their way out of a field they had known all their lives, unless they *turned their coats*, which action had the effect of releasing them from the spell.

In the heyday of genuine belief in the existence of fairies human intercourse with them was very frequent and led to surprising consequences such as a man disappearing from sight for years and yet on return thinking he had but passed a night in Fairyland. Such an experience fell to the lot of Thomas the Rhymer in Scotland and from Welsh fairy-lore we learn of a man who on leaving a farm-house heard a little bird singing sweetly on a tree nearby. Enchanted by the strain he sat down to listen. When the song was over and he rose to his feet he observed that the tree under which he had rested was now withered and dead. On returning to his house he found it also changed and with a stranger in it, an old man who was angry when asked what he was doing there. 'You insult me by asking what I am doing in my own house!' cried the old man. 'In your own house?' faltered the young man. 'Where's my father and mother whom I left here but a few minutes ago while I listened to the music of a heavenly bird in yonder tree — leafy then, but withered now: all changed as is this house?' 'Your name?' asked the old man trembling. 'John.' 'Poor John! I heard my grandfather who was your father often speak of you, and long did he bewail your loss. Fruitless inquiries were made for you, vain searchings; but old Catti Madlen of Brechfa declared that you were under the power of the fairies, and that you would not be released until the last sap of that sycamore tree was dried up. Embrace, embrace my dear uncle, your nephew!' The old man stepped forward to embrace him, but at that moment he crumbled into dust.

§ IV  THE  WOOD-SPIRITS  OF  GREECE
AND ROME

THESE wood-spirits met with in the folk-lore of Northern Europe belong to the same class of beings who on a large scale were so famously celebrated by the Greeks and the Romans. At first they did not appear in a very appealing guise. Their evolution was a progressive humanization. The nymphs and naiads, fit company for the highest Gods of Olympus, came last. First were seen the centaurs and the cyclops. Dwelling on Mount Pelion, the offspring of a cloud and a murderer, the centaurs were called savage monsters by Homer, and later were represented as half horses and half men, until they met their match at the hand of Hercules. Yet all of them were not thought of as savage. Thus Chiron was regarded as wise and just, as well he might be since he was the son of Cronos who deprived his father, Uranus, of the government of the world, and was in turn dethroned by his son, Zeus, the mightiest of the Olympians. Chiron reaping advantage from personal instruction given him by Apollo and Artemis became renowned for his skill in hunting, medicine, music, gymnastics, and the art of prophecy, and was able to claim as his own pupils the heroes Jason, Castor, Pollux, Peleus, and Achilles. And yet in spite of the remarkable and accomplished Chiron, the centaurs were generally feared as wild and terrible creatures of the forest whose weapons were uprooted trees and whose presence was assumed in the whirlwind and the storm. The cyclops, according to Hesiod, were Titans of the woods, sons of Uranus and Ge, each with one circular eye in the centre of the forehead; while Homer represents them as devouring human beings. Thrown into Tartarus by Cronus, they were rescued by Zeus to whom they showed their gratitude by furnishing him with thunderbolts and lightning. Later they were found in the woods of Sicily as assistants to Hephaestus whose workshop was Mount Etna's volcano.

The centaurs and cyclops were succeeded in time by beings who were half men and half goats, known as satyrs and sileni, while under the name of Pan a class of doubtfully amicable wood-spirits evolved into a quite benevolent god. The son of a nymph, Pan was called 'god of the wood' and 'companion of kids' and 'goat-herd'. He was represented with horns and goats' legs, standing beside a sacred oak or pine, a fir-wreath on his head and a branch in his hand. He revelled among the satyrs and piped among the nymphs; he roamed on the mountains and hunted game in the valleys. The Arcadians called him the Lord of the Woods. For the most part he was considered friendly to man and the protector of herds. The sounds of his revelry were heard from afar; but sometimes they were incomprehensible and alarming, and all who heard them were filled with panic. Born of Hermes by a nymph of Arcadia, Pan's personal appearance was symbolic of Nature. His horns called to mind the rays of the sun and the curves of the moon; his spotted faun-skin reflected the stars in the sky; his lower limbs were like unto the trees and the beasts; his feet were goat-like in token of the stability of the earth and his pipe and reeds in accordance with the harmony of heaven.

The satyrs might be described as degraded editions of Pan, malicious and sensual, coarse in feature, bestial in form, demoniacal in character and closely connected with Dionysus, forming part of his Bacchanalian train. The fauns and silvani of Italy were the counterpart of Pan and the satyrs of Greece. The nymphs, on the other hand, appeared to the Greeks as beautiful female forms — who were also called Dryads, and when stationed in trees, forming part of trees, called Hamadryads.

The nymphs, free to go where they wished, not being confined to any particular tree, gathered many legends around their name. They had relations with both men and gods. Thus, in Messapia, some shepherds beholding a company of nymphs dancing round a tree, rashly challenged them to a contest, and on being vanquished were turned into a grove. Nymphs were held in great respect by the Olympian Gods who frequently fell in love with them. Apollo was so attracted by a nymph called

Dryope that she bore him a son, and by another called Cyrene who bore him Aristaeus, the inventor and first keeper of bees. Pan also had his loves but was ill-received by them, and on one occasion when he took a nymph in his arms he found she had turned into reeds. For this world of gods and lesser deities strikes curiously against our reasoning minds. It seems a confusion of powers. The gods could work what miracles they pleased; yet they were often in trouble and frequently acted as if they had no such powers. It is extremely difficult to follow the actions and calamities of a single one of them. They behaved like ordinary human beings only more so, though their miraculous powers did not seem much use to them in their frequent quarrels and feuds both among themselves and with mortals. If Cronos, for instance, had the power to throw the cyclops into the pit of Tartarus, why should not Zeus have been able to provide his own thunderbolts? Again, when a shepherd called Terambos derided the advice of some nymphs they changed him into a cockchafer, and when the hunter, Picus, declined the attentions of Circe she changed him into a woodpecker; but when Echo spurned the god, Pan, he could do nothing; and neither could she do anything when Narcissus refused her hand, save slowly pine away into a sound of lamentation that can still be heard echoing in rocky woodlands; but the god, Nemesis, found no difficulty in causing Narcissus to become so enamoured of his own face mirrored in a pool that he died of grief at the unattainable felicity of possession and was metamorphosized into the flower which bears his name. Perhaps Echo was too fond of Narcissus to work him harm by way of metamorphosis; and in comparison it is interesting to note the cruelty of Artemis when she saw Actaeon, the celebrated hunts-

55

man, watching her from the bank of a pool in which she was bathing. Her modesty was so outraged that she instantly turned him into a stag with the result that he was torn to pieces by fifty of his own dogs — an example of imperfect justice perhaps fit to be compared with the action of King Maon of Ireland who, possessing the ears of a horse, thought it proper every time he had his hair cut to order the execution of his barber.

There was no end to these classic fancies: we are all familiar with their beautiful embroidery. It was not fancy to them. Their minds had not reached the stage when they could imagine a single creator. It was not possible that the splinterer of the crag was also the shaper of the oak. Did He who made the lamb make thee? is a *cri de cœur* even now not yet wholly spent. Looking round upon the rich and lovely lands of Greece and Italy, under those smiling heavens, beside those silver floods, they beheld a multitude of spiritual toilers so many and various that according to Ovid there were one hundred alone in the River Anio . . . But our tale is confined to trees. As distinguished from the nymphs or dryads free to move about, there were the Hamadryads who dwelt in trees, were fixed in them, and were indeed so much part of them that they were sometimes imagined as female to the waist while their lower extremities were roots or trunks, much as a mermaid is half a fish. They were much venerated by gods and men, and we are told that Aphrodite entrusted her infant Aeneas — whose father was a mortal — to the care of the Hamadryads of the wooded Ida. In a famous hymn to Aphrodite, Homer speaks of them as being neither mortal nor divine but as tasting immortal food and mating with sileni and the sons of Zeus; and that at their birth lofty pines and oaks spring up and flourish on the mountains, and when death overtakes them the branches of the trees fall down, the bark withers, the trunk decays and the souls of the nymphs leave the light of the sun.

In Homer's hymn it is the oak and the pine which are inhabited by the spirits; but amongst the names of nymphs who have been handed down are also Philyra, the linden; Daphne, the laurel; Rhoea, the pomegranate; and Helike, the willow. It was believed that blood would flow if such a tree was injured. It was seen to bleed and to cry out if cut by the axe. Ovid put this into poetic form when he recounted how a Dryad-oak was felled by Eresicthon. He it was who dared to violate the immemorial shades of Ceres' sacred grove, and taking his axe approached a huge and ancient oak therein. Nymphs dwelling round the tree warned him not to touch it; but refusing to stay his hand he buried his axe within it. At which, sings Ovid:

> The trembling tree sent forth an audible groan!
> From its pale leaves and acorns died the green,
> Dark oozing sweat from every branch distilled,
> And as the scoffer smote it, crimson-red
> Gushed forth the wounded bark the sap, as streams
> When at the altar falls some mighty bull
> The life-blood from his neck.
>              Then from its heart
> Issued a voice, 'Thou strikest in this trunk
> A nymph whom Ceres loves, and for the deed
> Dearly shalt pay. With my last voice thy doom
> I prophesy, and in thy imminent fate
> Find solace for my own.'

And indeed she was avenged. Ceres made Eresicthon so hungry that he devoured his own limbs.

WE have spoken of demons and lesser deities. But how about the Gods of Olympus themselves? What was their origin? When we pass in review the great gods that have come down to us, still carrying with them something of their magic in the very sound of their names, we find that most of them started as trees, if we may put it that way. They developed into greater and grander persons in the minds of their devotees, but in the first instance they grew from trees, or were trees. Though eventually they held court upon the Mountain in all the panoply of deified beings, they could not have got there without benefit of the oak, the ivy, the apple, and the mistletoe.

Thus with Zeus. How came he into the world? Where his cradle? What the steps by which he climbed to the immortal mount? Let us see: there is a terrible noise in the sky; the thunder speaks; it is a god, it is indeed a god of gods, the most powerful of all. He who can shake the earth to its foundations. What is his external aspect, his visible incarnation? See yonder tree — an OAK. Look at its branches — shaped in similitude with the lightning that is scored on the sky when the thunder speaks. Yes, the twisted branch of flame that is traced on the dark screen of night is mirrored here in the contorted branches of the oak.[1] There is the habitation of the god, the Thunder-god himself.

That was the first step. The oak became personified thunder. Then a further step. For who is this, holding converse with the thunder-tree? The Red-Headed

---

[1] Moreover, according to Frazer, Rendell Harris and Worde Fowler, the oak is more often thunder-struck than other trees — Thrice as often as the pine, ten times as often as the beech.

Woodpecker is seen tapping. A wonderful being, and fitly apparelled for one who keeps acquaintance with the gods. But stay! — this is no lackey, no friend or messenger, he is the God of Thunder himself.

Thus in animal form the Thunder-god is projected and becomes detached from the tree. As time goes on he becomes ever more removed from his origin in the plant and then from his origin as the Thunder-Bird, and becomes a Thunder-Man and a Thunder-God who as he evolves in the imagination of the people becomes ever further detached from his foundations until he gradually ascends from the floor of earth and takes his place as the mightiest of the gods on Mount Olympus, holding in his hands the government of the world.

Thus with Dionysus. Behind him stands the ivy. See the ivy that clings about the oak. That was the beginning of the God of Wine. A strange entrance perhaps for the Bacchanalian Spirit with his train of riotous revellers with vine-leaves in their hair. But mark the god-building evolution. The oak was thunder. Animistic belief turned everything that thunder touches into thunder — tree, bird, or bee. And that which grows on the oak is thunder. Therefore the ivy is thunder. And when the time comes for the animistic god-makers to project a lesser thunder-deity from the parasite on the oak, then Dionysus will be that god. In the words of Rendell Harris — 'When the phytomorph becomes the anthropomorph, the name of the new (subordinate) thunder-deity is Dionysus. In other words, *Dionysus is the ivy*; in the first instance, he is ivy, nothing more or less.'[1] Only later did the vine (and other parasites) become entwined with his name, and other elements, ritual and orgiastic, become part of the Ivy Cult.

[1] RENDELL HARRIS, *The Ascent of Olympus.*

Thus with Apollo. Behind him stand the oak, the apple tree, and the mistletoe. The genesis of the god can be traced to the mistletoe on the apple tree — he was a projection from it, as Dionysus was a projection from the ivy, and Zeus from the oak. Foremost amongst the powers of Apollo was that of healing — for the mistletoe was the All-healing herb of Antiquity. 'Apollo is a personified All-heal, and to his primitive apparatus of mistletoe berries, bark, and leaves, he has added a number of simples, more or less all-heals, or patent-medicines, which taken together constitute the Garden of Apollo, the original apothecary's shop.' I take that from Rendell Harris, who by sheer force of character, style, wit, instance, detail, and data carries the day in these matters; but of course it is also a fact that the laurel was as sacred to Apollo as the oak to Zeus and that his wor-shippers attended no rites without a crown of laurel on their heads and a branch in their hands, and that the poet received inspiration and the prophet intuitive powers through the laurel staff which they carried.

Thus with Artemis. Behind her stands the mugwort. She too, before ascending the exalted hill, must rise from a plant. Just as Apollo can be traced to the mistletoe, his cult as healer and master of wizardry proceeding from the medicinal value of the mistletoe and certain other plants in his medical garden, so Artemis in her garden, with her medicine for women at child-birth and her herbs that are helpful and herbs that are fatal, goes back to the mugwort and starts on her journey as personified medicine. We can appreciate the urge to personify a powerful herb as to personify thunder. If few pheno-mena seemed — and still seem — more tremendous than thunder, nothing throughout the ages has so filled the minds of men with credulity and wild hope as medicinal properties. The expectation of cure in those early days did not rely only upon herbs; oils, odours, and unguents no less than the products of rust, lime, corals, and sponges were estimated medically; the blood of gladiators and the brains of babies had great medical value, while any man's spittle was a protection against serpents, and the hair of his head could be used for a method of warding off gout; the blood of an elephant cured rheumatism, and ants' eggs a disordered stomach as surely as a toothache could be stopped by use of a stag's horn, a cough cured by wolf's liver, an ulcer or an earache healed by the ashes of a mouse mixed with honey, and many kinds of sores got rid of by binding a green lizard upon your person. We cannot suppose that these remedies were always effective. But there is reason to believe that the mugwort was often a wonderful panacea as well as the mother of herbal practice. That discovery must have been hailed with genuine relief, and it is not difficult to suppose that the people were glad to attend at the birth of a goddess. That was her origin, her main root. Afterwards the further fancy of the image-makers was free to play around her cult, and many other plants became associated with her name. Just as Zeus became more than the oak-god of Dodona and took upon himself the duties of a god of agriculture and accepted vegetable offerings, so Artemis also widened her scope and became associated with the cedar and the nut tree in Arcadia, with the myrtle in Laconia, with the willow in Sparta, while in Achea she was worshipped as the guardian of the woodlands and the nurturer of the hyacinth.

Thus with Aphrodite. Behind her stands the mandrake. This plant made a great impression upon the Ancients. Its root was supposed to be shaped in human form, a grotesque parody of a man or of a woman, the famous 'forked radish' of Falstaff. It was so alarming and dangerous a personality and it shrieked so loudly when pulled[1] that men dared not pluck it up themselves and employed a dog to do so, who then expired in agony. According to experts in the matter it was rarely to be found anywhere except under a gallows, where the humours and juices of the victim — especially if innocent — falling upon the root gave it human form. For as we know, belief in weal for all through the woe of martyrs, belief in the blood of the innocent shed for the guilty, answers a deep desire in the human heart. The good which the juice of the mandrake (or mandragora) had in store for men was of a pleasing nature. It was a love-potion. Of all the simples in the herbalist's shop, that which derived from this terrible root was the most potent in the promotion of the affections; so much so that it was only an Othello for whom not poppy nor mandragora, nor all the drowsy syrups of the East could ease his pain. Bit by bit the idolators got to work in the graving of their Image until at last Aphrodite in Greece and Venus in Italy rose from this root to receive the worship and enjoy the adoration of the people. Thus another of the immortal gods was made by mortal men, and the bright priestess of love who smiles on us from heaven must first be dug from out the darkness of the earth. For no god deserves the name who has not feet of clay.

§ VI THE WIDESPREAD WORSHIP OF TREES

WE begin to catch some glimpse of the complexity of tree mythology. There were the demons in the forests, the offspring of fear; there were lesser spirits of all

[1] See *Romeo and Juliet*, Act IV, Sc iii, l. 48 '... shrieks like mandrakes torn out of the earth'.

kinds, some amiable and light, offspring of fancy; there was that steady building-up of the great Olympians. But the total result of that fear and that fancy and that worship is hardly subject to straight description, for many spirits were not in distinct categories; there was considerable confusion, and in placing these beings before you with some degree of clarity I may do violence to the actuality of the entanglement. The spirits were sometimes generic, sometimes individual; demons evolved into gods and gods into demons. There is constant evolution. Today the tree is the body, tomorrow the abode of a spirit — animism turning into polytheism. Thus we see the Wild Huntsman of North America, known as Heno, riding the clouds and splitting the forest trees with his thunderbolts; and then we see him, later, gathering the clouds together and pouring down warm rain — as a god of agriculture. Many single spirits developed into a general Spirit of Vegetation; and often enough, I feel sure, in the mind of the primitive, several different conceptions existed at the same time. Nevertheless, we can say definitely that *tree-worship*, as distinct from fear of demons and belief in sprites, was spread throughout the world.

We turn to Egypt. Osiris, their god of vegetation, had his origin in a tree as also Adonis in Syria and Attis in Phrygia. He watched over the crops, assisted at their growth, and protected them from evil influences. In early days the acacia was intimately associated with Osiris, and we find inscribed on an ancient sarcophagus the device: 'Osiris shoots up.' The Ancient Egyptian monuments depict his dead body as enclosed in a tree, and tradition fostered a ceremony in which a pine tree was cut down and the centre hollowed out into a hole in which an image of Osiris was placed — a remarkably clear expression, as Frazer points out, of the idea that a tree is tenanted by a personal being.

There were — and still are — some wonderful sycamore fig trees of luxuriant growth seen to flourish in the Egyptian desert — a strange greenness in the sand. Beautiful — yet perhaps not strange to us: for we know that though they are miles distant from the Nile, the river has infiltrated through to them, and that they really stand with their feet in the water. The Egyptians considered them to be divine and animated with goddesses who were sometimes pleased to manifest themselves so that their heads and even their whole bodies would emerge from the trunk of the tree, then re-enter it, becoming re-absorbed — or, according to the Egyptian expression, the trunk *ate* them again. These tree-goddesses, known as Hâthor, Nuit, Selkît, and Nit, were believed to provide nourishment for their devotees on earth, and Egyptian vases represent them as bending over and pouring out water from a vessel and milk from their breasts — (for the sycamore fig, when cut, produces a milky fluid). *The Book of the Dead*, of the Ancient Egyptians, gave elaborate instructions to all souls embarked on their long and arduous journey to the Islands of the Blest. The soul, on leaving the body, set out resolutely, staff in hand, to climb the hills and cross the desert; and when at last weary and faint with hunger and thirst, he reached the divine sycamores, then one of the goddesses — Nuit, Hâthor, Selkît or Nit — emerged from a tree and offered him fruit, bread, and water. Thus refreshed he could proceed on his journey 'through lands of terror, infested by serpents and ferocious beasts, intersected by marshes and ponds where gigantic monkeys cast their nets';[1] but being now the guest of the

[1] J. H. PHILPOT, *The Sacred Tree.*

goddesses he passed safely through all perils and eventually reached the Islands of the Blest where he found happiness and peace for evermore.

We turn to India. Just as when we look at the Egyptian sycamores fed by the underground waters of the Nile we understand scientifically what they understood transcendentally, so the following incident rather charmingly illustrates the same sort of thing. When living in Tessore, Dr. Fergusson one day came upon a huge crowd that had gathered round a tree. It grew larger every day. He was told that a god had appeared in the tree. He approached it and found it hung with garlands and offerings. (In fact some good business was being done in offerings and Pûjâ). When Dr. Fergusson inquired in what manner the god manifested his presence he was told that soon after the sun rose the tree raised its head to welcome the god, and when evening came it bowed its head down again. Deciding to test this miracle the doctor found that it was even so. The tree did raise and lower its head. The explanation was not difficult. 'The tree had originally grown across the principle pathway through the village, but at last hung so low that in order to enable people to pass under it, it had been turned aside and fastened parallel to the road. In the operation the bundles of fibres which composed the the root had become twisted like the strands of a rope. When the morning sun struck on the upper surface of these, they contracted in drying, and hence a tendency to untwist, which raised the head of the tree. With the evening dews they relaxed, and the head of the tree declined, thus proving to the man of science, as to the credulous Hindu, that it was due to the direct action of the Sun God.'[1]

[1] A. PORTEOUS, *Forest Folklore.*

The intracacies of tree-worship in India would make a study in itself, and neither here nor anywhere else in this volume do I make the faintest attempt at an exhaustive statement. The great god, Brahma, who letting the light of his countenance fall upon chaos dispelled the primeval gloom and lifted the earth from the ocean, is represented in Hindu theology as having emanated from a golden lotus which had been quickened into life when the spirit of Om moved on the face of the waters. In the eyes of the Brahminical worshippers, the very essence of the deity was understood to descend into his tree. And Count Keyserling reminds us, in his *Travel Diary*, how for centuries the people believed, and still believe, that if they kneel under a tree sacred to Brahma, and repeat endlessly, the holy syllable OM, which is said to embody the ultimate meaning of the world, they can induce in themselves that condition which is favourable to the realization of Atman.

We turn to Northern Europe. There we find the tree held just as sacred. We see Thor associated with the rowan whose bunched berries in autumn still astonish us like flaming flowers, and then considered holy and sacred to the Finns. We see Ukho, their god of thunder, and Taara, and Balder all taking their origin from the oak. We see the sacred grove of Upsala dedicated to Woden, the god who after hanging for nine nights on the gallows tree descended to the underworld and brought back the prize of wisdom.

We turn elsewhere. It matters little where we turn. From Arabia where the goddess, Al-Ozza, received through her sacred acacia offerings of eggs, to Mexico where the god Huitzilopochtli at the Feast of Teteionan was placated by the head of a woman whose flayed skin was draped round a naked youth; from Persia where

Ormuzd, speaking to Zoraster, says — 'Go, O Zoraster, to the living trees, and let thy mouth speak before them these words: *I pray to the pure trees, the creatures of Ormuzd*', to France where at Marseilles, in primitive times, human sacrifices were made to trees; from the sacred trees of Japan bound with fillets of straw rope in acknowledgment of their tenancy by divine spirits, to the enormously widespread ceremonial worship in groves by the people of ancient Germany; from one end of the world to the other we trace the unexampled power of trees over the minds of men. And perhaps no race was more influenced than the Jews. So deeply did the Semites cling to the belief that there was a spiritual force inherent in vegetation, that the Old Testament prophets, engaged in removing the Deity out of reach, were appalled at the perversity with which the Israelites persisted in planting groves and setting up altars in the sacred shades.

We turn to Ceylon where we find the Bo Tree of the Buddha. The conception here is not quite the same. It is more advanced: it is less a question of a god-in-a-tree than a tree of enlightenment. It was the tree that bestowed wisdom. Gautama, the great philosopher, the good man, the compassionate soul who sorrowed for humanity, the noble searching mind that sought the truth — did he not sit under a tree from whence he rose to save mankind from the stings of reality? Was it not a holy thing, that tree, was it not divine? Many are the legends that have gathered round its name. There was such a man. There was such a tree under the shade of which he sat in meditation. For how long? A few hours, perhaps a day; perhaps a day and a night. That was long enough for him to resolve the tension, to face the tempter, and accept the cup. Then he felt the call and saw the way and moved across the screen of history. As always, the truth, the actual fact, is wonderful enough. But men must add to it and try to make it more. So here. The legends tell how Gautama 'sat for six years in absolute solitude under the tree, in utter abandonment to his sublime meditations. While there, the demoniacal hosts assailed him, surrounding the tree, invoking hurricanes and darkness, bringing deluges of rain and hurling fiery darts at him. Buddha triumphantly repelled these attacks and in the end the demons fled discomfited. Thus was Buddha enabled to retain possession of the tree with all its knowledge and wisdom'.[1] For men did not consider that a man himself could shine: the light must come from outside and be the gift of gods or trees or tree-gods.

. . . And yet, even today, though we have lowered the external flags and cast aside the baubles like growing children dropping dolls, we do not throw aside the Bo Tree as a symbol. It is the symbol for us still of how trees promote *meditation*. Their silence is almost like unspoken thoughts. They are indeed the friends of philosophers. We enter the wood. We leave behind the world that is so much with us — it has wholly gone. We tread the silent glades in silence. Here is the reign of peace. Here the mind is suddenly purified. See that noble old oak. There is a place for meditation! Beneath those shady boughs, in the stillness of that room, shall we not come to truth? Could we sit long enough, we feel, in this untrespassed calm, and balk the screaming duties that are not real within these gates, and flaunt the CLOCK that we call time — then we too would be enlightened. One man did sit long enough under a tree to achieve this, and it is not strange that his tree has been venerated ever since, and that a cutting from it, planted in 245 B.C., is still

[1] J. H. PHILPOT, *The Sacred Tree.*

carefully tended by his disciples. The hands that planted it are long since quenched in dust, but it knows nothing of death. The longevity of trees alone would be sufficient to make them seem as gods, and we can still appreciate the ancient sculptures representing the adoration of the bodhi tree in which its trunk is surrounded by a pillared erection with niches containing umbrellas, and with elephants bringing garlands to hang on its branches.

§ VII FEAR OF INJURING TREES : STRANGE
OFFERINGS

THE belief that a god dwelt in a tree, or that the tree was the spirit, naturally made the cutting down of trees a very anxious and nervous affair. If the holy basil of India was believed by the Hindus to be pervaded by the divinity of Vishnu and of his wife, Laksmi, it is easy to understand the conviction that those who uprooted it would be punished by the offended deity; if the Wanika of Eastern Africa believed that every tree had its spirit, it is not surprising that the destruction of a coco-nut tree, which provided them with so much nourishment, was regarded as equivalent to matricide; if it was believed, as in Dalmatia, that whoever felled one of the great beeches or oaks would die on the spot, again we need not wonder that such trees were left untouched. Many races, especially the Germanic and the Scandinavian, believed that the express duties of certain wood-spirits consisted in looking after the forest and shielding the trees from injury. They were coloured green, and their skin was of a mossy texture, though sometimes they appeared in the guise of men and women. One of them, Pulch of the Kammerforst, chastised those who stole wood; another, called Hylde-moer, believed to reside in the elder, avenged all injuries done to his habitation, and anyone wishing to cut so much as a branch must first ask his permission or be subject to misfortune.

When it was absolutely necessary to make a clearing the spirits could often be appeased by suitable gifts and apologies. Some trees, of course, were too sacred to be touched on any account, such as the holy groves of the Cheremiss tribe that once existed in Russia — groves that contained trees so divine that if touched by some unknown hand could only be appeased by other members of the tribe taking a goose, torturing it to death and then throwing it on the fire, while they prayed to the gods to punish the sinner and cause him to perish like the bird. There was nothing vague concerning this fear of the various tree-gods. Did they not hear a loud cry coming from the trunk when they had the temerity to use an axe? And were they not sometimes appalled to see a serpent or a blue bull glide or rush from a falling tree?

Nevertheless many of the spirits could be appeased if proper measures were taken. The precautions ranged according to the supposed demands of the various tree-gods. Some appeared to require the sacrifice of a dog, a cock, and a cow; others were believed to be content with a libation of goat's blood; some needed the decapitation of a hen on the fresh-cut stump; others demanded that nails of gold or silver should first be driven into the trunk of the chosen tree. Occasionally it seems that woodmen engaged in making a clearing thought it sufficient to leave some trees standing, with the hope that the ejected spirits would be content to change their habitation. The Alfoors of Poso, in Central Celebes, did no more than simply beseech the spirit to leave his abode and go elsewhere, and to that end deposited food at the foot of the tree as provision for the journey. 'Woe to the luckless wight', says Frazer, 'who should turn a tree-spirit out of his house without giving him due notice!' The Toboongkoos not only gave fair warning to the spirits when about to clear a space of forest, they built a small house, and having furnished it with clothes and food and gold they then offered it as a new residence for all the spirits forced to vacate their premises. The Tomori were even more thoughtful, and placed little ladders against the trunks to enable the spirits to descend in safety and comfort. Sometimes a frank appeal was made to the tree-god to take it in good part. Thus the inhabitants of Sumatra would assure the tree they were about to cut down that it was the Dutch authorities who forced them to do it, and if they didn't they would be hanged. Abyssinian woodcutters, on hearing the crack of a tree about to fall after cutting, and thinking it to be the tree itself groaning, would hasten to explain that not they but an elephant or a rhinoceros had caused it to fall. And there is something touching in the custom of the Indian priest who, obliged to cut down a tree for a sacrificial post, was instructed by the Satapatha-brâh-mana to place a blade of darbha-grass between the axe and the tree, saying: 'Oh, grass shield it!' and then, before striking, to cry: 'Oh, axe, hurt not!'

Some trees were thought to be inhabited by the spirits of the dead, and tribes often carefully preserved a tree into which the souls of the villagers entered at death — a sacred tree was never cut down or injured without dire penalty. It is well known that one of the most powerful influences amongst early races, not to mention the Chinese up to the present century, was a boundless respect for ancestors. And of course they too dwelt in trees. The biggest tree in a village was regarded as their headquarters, and treated as temple or shrine. Such homes of ancestors were countless, and in every case the fear of any disrespect shown even to a single branch of such a tree was such that not only were offerings continually made, but injury to them meant certain calamity to the desecrator, while if they were ever cut down the whole village would surely perish. Sometimes the trees were considered as more than the houses of the ancestors: in some cases they were the ancestors. Thus the belief, held so often and in so many places, in numerous re-incarnations, led to the conviction that souls, between each new appearance in the world, resided in a tree or were transformed into trees — for the terrible beliefs of men are as many as they are merciless.

It was not always considered sufficient to offer an apology or a prayer to the indwelling spirit. The Siamese had such a veneration for the takhun tree that they offered it cakes and rice before felling it; and even so, such was their dread of offending the spirit, that all necessary tree-cutting was relegated to the lowest criminals. In Mexico the cypress was decorated with votive offerings of teeth, ribbons, and locks of hair. In Russia, up to the fourteenth century, the influence of the tree-gods over the herds was so firmly held that it was the custom to appease them with the sacrifice of a cow, while in Esthonia the peasants poured fresh bullock's blood about the roots of sacred trees in order that the cattle might thrive. Indeed, the gifts hung upon the branches or placed beside the trunks of trees make sufficiently emphatic proof of how real was the veneration and how immediate the fear. The gifts were carefully chosen with a view to the taste of the deity. Thus in Arabia, the sacred acacia which was the dwelling-place of the goddess Al-Ozza, was hung once a year with spears, skirts, and eggs. Some deities were thought to prefer food only, and the Egyptians would place upon the sycamores presents of figs, grapes, and cucumbers. Other tree-gods were found to favour gifts of the chase, as we see by studying the vases and sculptured tablets of the Greeks: and we learn from an historian of the second century B.C. of a celebrated tree laden with bows and arrows, the heads of boars and the skins of lions. 'The rich brought their jewels, the poor their homely tools and utensils', writes Mrs. J. H. Philpot. 'The fisherman dedicated his nets in gratitude for an exceptional catch. The shepherd offered his flute as a welcome gift to Pan. Some of the dedicatory inscriptions preserve for us the pathos of the gift. 'Daphnis, the flute-player, bowed with shaking age, has here dedicated his shepherd's staff, too heavy for his weak hand, to meadow-loving Pan.' 'Lais, grown old, hangs her too truthful mirror on the sacred tree of Aphrodite. Take it, O lovely Cytherea; to thee alone is undying beauty given.' In the same way Bacchic revellers, their frenzy past, brought to the tree the cymbals, robes, and perfumed tresses they had used.

It is a strange tale to us. Here were all these gods. They were supposed to appreciate these gifts. Yet they never touched them. They never wore those garments, they never ate that food. All the presents presumably rotted on the branches — for the receivers did not exist. Yet from generation to generation fresh offerings were made. Evidently it was not necessary for these beings to pass through the hollow form of actually existing in the flesh, since they could be heard in the many noises of the forest and seen in the strange shapes that often must have seemed ghost-like or god-like — but it baffles our

c*

consciousness how the devotees accounted for their gifts never being taken and used by these remarkably definite gods. And, indeed, in spite of what I have just said about the existence of the gods being accountable for by queer noises and shapes, the continuousness and thoroughness of their palpable appearance is extraordinary. Some of the demi-deities, the nymphs, were said to marry mortal men on occasion and only fade away when by mischance their special tree was cut down. Some of the big deities in the Grecian pantheon did likewise. It is difficult to see how this sort of thing could be believed in without the concrete appearance of the god. An invisible oracle is one thing: an invisible husband is another.

Still, the fact that we stumble is no reason to doubt the ability of earlier minds to move freely in these fields. Human nature may not change very much, but the mind does — a fact of intense importance to us all, calling for the consideration and understanding of each fresh generation of thinkers. I confess that were it not for the light it throws upon the human mind I would not spend ten minutes reading Greek Mythology. Its inconsequence is too near the silliness of a Silly Symphony. To us the strange thing about the Greek gods is that they were not gods in our sense. They were conditioned; they lived on earth; they held direct relationship with men. But they had supernatural powers. Yet, as I suggested earlier, there seems no sense in these powers sometimes. Thus, Apollo kept oxen. No harm in that — however curious to us. Let us grant him his oxen. Enter Hermes, son of Zeus, aged three hours. On seeing these quadrupeds he springs from his cradle and steals them, driving them from Pieria to Pylos. Apollo is surprised to find the oxen gone; but possessing great prophetic powers, he divines who stole them. He goes to

Cyllene where he finds Hermes in his cradle. He carries him before Zeus who compels the baby to return the animals. But Hermes at this moment suddenly plays the lyre with such unexampled skill that Apollo, charmed by the brilliant infant, is pleased to present him with the oxen.

Such is but one of the exploits of the gods, considered too childish by the children of this age who even dismiss the Heroes as 'success stories'. But it should surely be part of our education to give these things our attention, so that, in a simple and amusing form we can grasp the fact that consciousness develops. At first there was this firm belief in a multiplicity of supposedly visible gods, powerful but conditioned and behaving like mortals. For centuries it satisfied the mental and spiritual needs of man. Gradually this scheme fell out of favour and eventually the conception of one god was substituted. This god had the great merit of being invisible and un-conditioned. He dwelt on no hill. He kept no oxen. Being by himself, there was no trouble with rival or col-league gods — (save when given races each projected a deity, and the followers of each fought each other). At last he came to be described in the West as having neither body, parts, nor passions. But the description was not popular up to at least the end of the nineteenth century, and as the desire for 'a personal god' continued to be expressed the administers of religion did their best to meet the demand, sometimes even going further than necessary and in seasons of drought frankly calling upon the god of rain to relieve the situation, while in January 1945, during the flying bomb menace, clergymen asked the god of war to give his protection to *Southern England*. In neither case was the deity actually designated in particular as god of rain or war but was addressed as falling under the general head of God; and since it was assumed that if he might be prevailed upon to send rain at a proper time to a given place, it was fair to suppose that he would not be unwilling to keep his eye on Southern England, say between London and Portsmouth. In some parts of England a few people prefer to discard the Christian conception, and by dancing round a Maypole, restore a measure of tree-worship; while others, adapting Christianity to their idea — by means best known to themselves — engage a clergyman on Plough Monday to call upon the god of vegetation to lay his blessing on their crops. These pleasing and amiable practices which have the merit of bringing spiritual refreshment to simple souls, are unfortunately ineffective on any large scale since there is lacking the necessary conviction. In the range of human activity there is nothing more profoundly beautiful and upraising than a religious service. But in order to receive its benefit we must either take it literally or have a deep sense of its symbolic meaning. Today the majority of people can do neither. Both polytheism and monotheism have done their work. The images are broken, the idols are all overthrown. This is regarded now as a very irreligious age. But perhaps it only means that the mind is moving from one state to another. The next stage is not a belief in many gods. It is not a belief in one god. It is not a belief at all — not a conception in the intellect. It is an extension of consciousness so that we may *feel* God, or, if you will, an experience of harmony, an intimation of the Divine, which will link us again with *animism*, the experience of unity lost at the in-break of self-consciousness. This will atone for our sin (which means *separation*): it will be our at-one-ment.

I T was not only the great forest with all its echoing
mysteries and deep shadowy shrouds, nor the single
tree of compelling size or fearful aspect, which commanded the veneration and promoted the idolatry of
the people. A clump of trees made a great impression.
A few standing closely erect upon the hill suggested
divinity, and certainly appeared as fitting places in
which to worship. Sometimes they were supposed to be
the abode of gods, and sometimes they were regarded
simply as natural temples in which gods might be
approached. In both cases they were known as Groves.

The word is familiar to us. It hangs like a picture in
the room of memory for those of us whose childhood
came under the influence of Victorian piety. For the
Groves concealed idolatry in the days when idols of
any god save Jehovah were considered wicked; and that
period in the world's history covered by the Old Testament was so riddled with denunciation regarding groves
that centuries later the children in Europe were made
to learn about it. Sentences such as: 'He removed the
high places and brake the images and cut down the
groves', or: 'And they set them up images and groves in
every high hill and under every green tree', or: 'And they
left all the commandments of the Lord their God, and
made them molten images, even two calves, and made a
grove, and worshipped all the host of heaven, and served
Baal', or: 'And he set a graven image of the grove that
he had made in his house', and a great many more such
observations made hundreds of years B.C. were re-
delivered to Europeans hundreds of years A.D. As a boy
at school, aged ten, I remember being expected to pull
a solemn face over this, and under the head of 'divinity',

being made to learn by heart the imprecations of the prophets. This put me more against the prophets than the groves.

The Druids, on the other hand, hold some kind of fascination for us. There is evidently magic in the name. They held converse with most esoteric gods who forbade worship within walls or under roofs. Their rites were to be observed in the open air on high ground so that they might view the countries of the sky with unimpeded gaze. To this end they built sacred groves with the trees which they most revered, especially the oak — that tree of trees, that tree of strength and shade, that tree which from the birth to the twilight of the gods has served as their temple or their house, their idol or their altar. These sacred groves of the Druids were closely guarded against the intrusion of strangers by ditch or mound or moat. Then, in the dark secluded temple built with living trees, the Druids set up huge perpendicular stones around which and upon which rites and sacrifices were performed.

It is very natural that bunches of trees should have affected the minds of those who gazed upon the speaking silence of their mystery. The following simple statement by Seneca cannot be improved. 'If you come upon a grove of old trees that have shot up above the common height, and shut out the sight of the sky by the gloom of their matted boughs, you feel there is a spirit in the place, so lofty is the wood, so lone the spot, so wondrous the thick unbroken shade.' How easy, in the Age of Fancy, to people such places with the supernatural. The happy venerations of the Greeks and the Romans made their groves so sacred that even Xerxes when passing through Achea forbade his army to do any act of devastation in a grove dedicated to Jupiter.

'The deities of a thousand groves and a thousand streams', wrote Gibbon, 'possessed in peace their local and respective influence.' The legends that have come down carry us into further histories of magic and fantasia and wild imaginings. We pass into regions of the ancient mind when thoughts took shape and walked. What symbols have we here? what hidden meanings? We may assume the cold cloak of scholarship, but can we find our way in realistic understanding? Can we follow Circe into her thick grove of dismal willows and in any way divine her object in turning all who landed on her island into pigs? Can we sense the argument within the souls of men who saw Golden Apples hanging in the Hesperian Grove, and a Golden Fleece on an oak in Colchis within the Grove of Ares? Do we know that Serpent who sat within a grove dedicated to Juno, with the power to test the chastity of maidens?

Some groves were supposed to grow in the infernal regions; and it was in his descent into the Stygian Grove to see his father and learn his fate and that of his Roman descendants, that Aeneas sought assistance from the Sibyl of Cumae. She, having painted in telling terms, those subterranean woods and black winding floods in the silent halls of gloomy Tartarus, explains how first having swum the Stygian lake, he would find upon a certain tree a bough with leaves and twigs of gold sacred to infernal Juno;[1] and having found it, what he must do to pluck it off, and thus equipped be free to visit the realms of the dead.

The size of some of the groves can be gathered by the Grove of Daphne which was ten miles in circumference, composed of laurel and cypress trees forming avenues in the centre of which was a magnificent temple sacred to

[1] This is Frazer's Golden Bough itself.

Apollo and Diana, round which a town sprang up so given over to luxury and revels that Cassius the Commander of Roman veterans was obliged to forbid them entrance. Indeed the use of these temples varied according to the temperament or station of the devotees, so that on the one hand we find the Emperor Vitellius wasting his energies in the Grove of Aricinum and in seven months of gluttony and idleness consuming six millions of money, while on the other we hear of husbandmen in the Grove of Acuna adoring the goddess of repose after their exertions with the harvest.

The variety of devotion and practice is sufficiently illustrated by the above if we remember also the Grove of Upsala in which every ninth year elaborate human and animal sacrifices were offered to Thor, Odin, and Freya; the Grove of Hoddmimir, deep underground in the realms of Hel, which was the abode of sinless beings waiting to re-people the earth after the dread catastrophe prophesied to fall upon men; the Grove of the Simmones of Saxony into which no person was allowed to enter without first being bound with a chain in token of his unworthiness; the Grove of Feronia where the priests at the period of festival walked barefooted over burning coals; the Grove sacred to Diana in which wolves would follow a man licking his hands just as at Diomedes the wild beasts lost their ferocity and the lion lay down with the lamb; and the Grove of the Sabines where a woodpecker, perched on a wooden pillar, prophesied to the people.

Not only were groves in this manner places of devotion, but they also served as sanctuaries. The indwelling deity had the power to offer inviolable refuge to the persecuted. Thus on reaching the cypress grove on the Acropolis in Peloponnesus fugitives from justice con-

sidered themselves so free from molestation that they
hung their chains upon the trees as garlands. Yet the
consideration of the god was bestowed with balanced
justice; for if Orestes in his flight from the Furies could
seek and find protection from his pursuers beneath the
laurel sacred to Apollo, then it was just that Cleomenes
who burnt the sacred grove at Argos together with five
thousand fugitives therein, should have been visited with
madness. This right of sanctuary was widely believed
in not only in relation to groves but also to single trees
dedicated to deity. The Amazons after their rout at the
hand of Hercules found asylum beneath the holy tree at
Ephesus, and the legend of Dionysus standing amidst the
branches of a sacred tree while flames raged around him,
reminds us of Shadrach, Meshach, and Abed-nego who
walked unsinged within the fiery furnace.

There was a further use for groves. They were sometimes more even than the abode of a god, a house of
worship, or a place of refuge. A grove could also be a
centre from which a deity would give advice or make
prophesies — that is, an Oracle. A rustling could be
heard among the branches! Was it not a god speaking?
Soon they learnt to interpret his message through specialists in this kind of thing — priests. Moreover, the roots
of the trees were regarded as cords of communication
with the lower regions, the abode of departed spirits
who were informed with wisdom and knowledge of the
future. Hence the very deep roots of the Oak at Dodona,
reaching down even to Tartarus they thought, justified
that grove to be considered particularly qualified in
prophetic power.

The idea of certain trees here and there as having
special powers to help, detect, or advise was never unusual, and until quite late in the history of superstition

the maidens of Franconia were accustomed to go to a certain tree on St. Thomas's day and knock on its trunk three times, after which they heard, or expected to hear, an answering spirit from within inform them by responding knocks what kind of husbands they would have. Less oracular but equally helpful seems to have been the herb called *concordia* which was consulted by Piedmontese lovers who were in doubt whether to marry. The root is shaped in the likeness of two hands, each with its five fingers. If the herb which they found was discovered with the hands conjoined, then of course the omen was favourable — and unfavourable if the hands pointed different ways.

In classic times the thing was done officially on an elaborate scale, the two chief places which performed these offices being Dodona and Delphi. The Grove of Dodona has been claimed as the most striking instance and the most signal vestige of tree-worship. An ancient oak therein was believed to be the actual seat of Zeus whose responses were interpreted according to the rustling of its branches and the murmuring of the sacred spring which rose at its foot — and recently excavated leaden tablets, inscribed with the questions addressed to the god by his votaries, carry us back four hundred years before Christ. The famous oracle at Delphi was more of an earth-oracle than a tree-oracle, though it contained an element of both. Situated in a great rocky cleft at the foot of Mount Parnassus it was held to be the central pivot of the earth from which rose the waters of the Castalian spring. Here was the original seat of the earth-mother, Gaia, the first being who sprang from Chaos. A tree, the laurel, played an intrinsic if not so predominant a part as at Dodona, its function being shared by the fissure of the rocks and the sacred waters.

A temple to Apollo was erected within the grove, in the centre of which was an opening from whence an intoxicating vapour proceeded — a vapour so powerful that having once caused the convulsion of goats who had strayed to the mouth of the cave, it led the people to suspect the presence of deity. A tripod was erected over the chasm on which the priestess called Pythia took a seat whenever the oracle was to be consulted, and thus seated, chewing laurel leaves and waving a branch, chanted ecstatic utterances containing the revelations of Apollo which were then written down by priests and immediately turned into verse by a poet hired for the purpose. Thus Apollo's oracular function was inseparably bound up with the use of that tree and the laurel became a recognized instrument of prophecy; so that when at last the laurel trees had disappeared the oracle was silent, and word was sent to the Emperor Julian who had hoped to re-inaugurate the worship: 'Tell the king that the cunningly built chamber has fallen to the ground; Apollo no longer has bower or inspired laurel or prophetic spring; vanished is the talking water.'

The career of these oracles lasted about two thousand years, but at length they lost their influence through the chicanery of charlatans and the corruption of priests. But some trees were believed to speak directly without the medium of an agent, and it was thought natural that the Argonauts should have listened to the advice of a voice proceeding from the Grove of the Hesperides, or the Romans to have taken warning from a Speaking Tree to repair their ramparts against the invasion of the Gauls; while perhaps the most outstanding example of such a myth is the voice that is supposed to have spoken to Alexander the Great. Having come to Persia to receive the homage of the people, he was informed that a wonderful tree grew in the land, which had the power to prophesy a man's expectation of life. Hastening to it, filled with the hope of years that would crown his glory, the Conqueror put his question. And the answer came — that he had but fourteen years to live.[1]

## §IX THE UNIVERSE TREE: THE STAIRS TO HEAVEN

WE now come to the most remarkable tree of all — the Cosmogonic Tree. The mind craves order. The mind must have a scheme. Every age needs a cosmology. We have ours today, and we accept it without question. Standing on a balcony of an Irish hotel one evening, Bernard Shaw looked at the moon. A man approached and asked him how far away he thought it was. 'By the look of the thing,' replied Shaw, 'I should say about twenty miles.' He had expected to get a rise out of his questioner, but the latter got a rise out of him. 'As a matter of fact,' he rejoined, 'you are not far out: it is exactly twenty-one miles away.' Subsequently this gentleman used to send Shaw books in which he proved that the moon was only twenty-one miles distant from the earth. Shaw says that these books were just as convincing as the books of other astronomers proving that it was two hundred and thirty-nine thousand miles away. Far be it from me to make any comment upon this. But I sometimes wish that I myself were less gullible in the swallowing of scientific statements regarding the distance of the stars, or the speed of light, and more often felt inclined to ask for evidence when I am told that ten thousand particles are at play upon the point of a

[1] According to some accounts not a voice but only a sound came from the tree needing the interpretation of a priest.

particle which is so small that you cannot see it. But I
accept the cosmology of the day as quite in order.

So did our ancestors accept theirs at that period. When
now we look up into the sky we see the endless ether.
They saw a roof. Here, beneath their feet, was the earth:
there, above, was its roof — blue, scarfed, or sparkling
with jewels. A roof must be supported, otherwise it will
fall down. What then, they asked, is holding up the roof
of the world? They gave more than one answer to this
question. Some said it was a tortoise. Others, from the
same quarter — India — said it was a snake that bears
the world on its head, or an elephant that carries it on
its back. More often it was a mountain that pillared the
empyrean. There was a Chaldean 'mountain of the
world whose head rivalled the heaven' and whose foot
was in the ocean, and it is in allusion to this that Isaiah
represents the King of Babylon as boasting that he
would ascend into heaven and exalt his throne above
the stars of God, and sit upon the mount of congregation
in the uttermost parts of the north. When Atlas made
war upon Zeus unsuccessfully he was condemned by his
conqueror to bear heaven upon his head and hands — a
myth directly derived from the idea that the lofty
mountains supported the ceiling of the world.

We are all familiar with that figure of Atlas —
(although we generally see him as supporting the whole
of the world, not just the roof). We are less familiar
with the more widespread conception that it was a tree.
It would be difficult to say which ideas came first or
whether they all came together, but certainly the belief
in a Universe Tree seems to have arisen spontaneously
from most parts of the world. It came as a natural
thought. 'The idea of referring to the form of a tree
the apparent conformation of the universe', says Goblet

d'Alviella, 'is one of the most natural methods of reasoning which can occur to the savage mind.' Indeed it
seems much more likely that it arose impulsively rather
than derivately since the idea was found not only
among the Chaldeans and the Egyptians, the Persians
and the Hindus, and among the races of Northern
Europe no less than in China and Japan, but it turns
up in rudimentary form among the aborigines of America
and New Zealand — and in the neat mythology of the
Maoris we find that Rangi, the sky, was forcibly separated
from his wife, the universal mother, earth, by one of their
children, Tane Mahuta, father of the forests, who planting his head upon the earth, upheld the heavens with his
feet.

It would seem that a cloud-capped mountain should
be far the easiest thing to conceive as a pillar; and sometimes the tree was thought of as growing from a mountain
top. Nevertheless we must accept the fact that they
could imagine the existence of colossal trees. We need
only think of the sort of tree-picture frequently drawn
up by the Hebrew prophets to realize the imaginative
possibilities in those days. Making proper allowance for
the turgid and tautological rhetoric of the word-drugged
Jews, we must suppose that Ezekiel knew his audience
when he spoke of a tree 'whose height was exalted above
all the trees of the field, and his boughs were multiplied,
and his branches became long because of the multitude
of waters when he shot forth. All the fowls of heaven
made their nests in his boughs, and under his branches
did all the beasts of the fields bring forth their young,
and under his shadow dwelt all great nations'. Nor need
we suppose that Nebuchadnezzar was surprised by the
imagery of the dream which he confessed to Daniel: 'I
saw, and behold a tree in the midst of the earth, and the

height thereof was great. The tree grew and was strong, and the height thereof reached unto heaven, and the sight thereof to the end of all the earth. The leaves thereof were fair and the fruit thereof much, and in it was meat for all: the beasts of the field had shadow under it, and the fowls of the heaven dwelt in the boughs thereof, and all flesh was fed of it.'

The above pictures would serve as visions of a Universe Tree; but in still earlier times when the mind moved even more freely in creative mood there was really no boundary to the properties of the Tree. The grander the conception the easier to believe. It bestowed knowledge, wisdom, bliss. It could grant men courage and give women children. It was the ladder by which the dead could mount to heaven. It provided milk, water, dew, and rain. Its juice was intoxicating. Its seed was the progenitor from which all forms of life were created. Its trunk was the abode of gods who fed upon the ambrosia which gave eternal life. Its roots reached down into the lowest depths of the nether regions from whence rose the springs that gave water to the rivers of the world. Its boughs composed the scaffolding of the sky; its leaves were clouds, its fruit the stars — the sun and moon but baubles in its branches.

We may smile at such a cosmology. We can scarcely feel that it is less beautiful than our own, or less comforting. It will be remembered that Carlyle, beating up against the new scientific era, with its handmaid the industrial revolution; already sensing the shape of things which now have come; and reacting to the extraordinary machine terminology of the modern thinkers who now are so much too much with us, spoke of the most famous of all Universe Tree conceptions — the Scandinavian Yggdrasil Ash. 'All life is figured by them as a Tree.

Igdrasil, the Ash tree of Existence, has its roots deep down in the kingdoms of Hela or Death; its trunk reaches up heaven-high, spreads its boughs over the whole Universe: it is the Tree of Existence. At the foot of it, in the Death-kingdom, sit three *Normas*, Fates — the Past, Present, Future; watering its roots from the Sacred Well. Its "boughs" with their buddings and disleafings — events, things suffered, things done, catastrophes — stretch through all lands and times. Is not every leaf of it a biography, every fibre there an act or word? Its boughs are Histories of Nations. The rustle of it is the noise of Human Existence, onwards from of old. It grows there, the Human Passion rustling through it like the voice of the gods. It is Igdrasil, the Tree of Existence. It is the past, the present, the future; what was done, what is doing, what will be done; "the infinite conjugation of the verb *To Do*". Considering how human things circulate, each inextricably in communion with all — how the word I speak to you today is borrowed, not from the Ulfila the Moesogoth only, but from all men since the first man began to speak — I find no similitude so true as this of a Tree. Beautiful; altogether beautiful and great. The "Machine of the Universe" — alas, do but think of that in contrast!'[1]

Above, I used the phrase — It was the stairs by which the dead could climb to heaven. These people had definite ideas about Paradise. It was located quite near, occupying a given geographical area above the roof of the world. Just as the gods were shaped very much in the image of men, only more fortunate and less subject to pain and limitation, so Paradise was very much like the earth only better. It was a garden in which you

[1] *Heroes and Hero Worship.*

dwelt without hurt in the midst of peace and plenty, and where you could occupy yourself with similar pursuits you knew on earth, hunting and sowing and reaping the heavenly pastures. And since all early thought referred phenomena to the idea of a central tree, we find in all the pictures of Paradise a significant tree. In the Heaven of the Mohammedans there was the tree called *Tooba* which was so large that a man mounted on the swiftest horse could not ride round its branches in a hundred years. It afforded pleasant shade over all the land, while its boughs were laden with delicious food to be plucked at pleasure by the delighted inhabitants; and at its foot a river of milk, a river of water, a river of honey, and a river of wine flowed perpetually for the benefit of the blest.

So close at hand was this Paradise that you could climb up to it (in some cases without the necessity of dying) by means of the Cosmic Tree by which it was upheld — a ladder which was ultimately responsible for our own famous Jack and the Beanstalk. The ideas about this Paradise were as various as the fancies of the people. These Gardens of Delight, these Islands of the Blest, these Elysian Fields were not always conceived of in terms of a time to come, they were mixed with the idea of a time that had been, a Golden Age of the past. Happily it is no part of my business to unravel all this or to digress into a history of heavens; but rather to pay attention to the power of trees over the minds and the hearts of men. The Tree held its significance according to the temperament of its projectors. To the Buddhist it was simply a Tree of Enlightenment, to the Persian a Tree of Immortality; and again, when you had used it as a highway to heaven, there you would still find it, now in the form of Hospitality, as with the Mohammedans, offering food and shade and drink; and now, as with the Jews and their Garden of Eden, as a Tree of Temptation. All symbols are significant and some profound, and it is this last which holds our attention still, the symbol of the tempting tree in the Garden, the tree of good and evil, the tree of knowledge, the tree of consciousness, the forbidden tree through which we were expelled from the paradise of innocent ignorance, and took upon ourselves the burden of understanding.

§ X TREES INTO MEN: MEN INTO TREES

IF anyone had raised questions concerning the origin of mankind in the nineteenth century before the coming of Darwinism, the answer, we must suppose, would have contained some reference to that Garden of Eden together with a vague idea that the first two persons started there. It would not have been considered necessary to probe further — there they were in the Garden. But in earlier days there was more concern as to how they actually came into existence in the first place. And the answer was — *from a tree*. It seemed, as we have seen, natural to refer all difficult problems to trees for solution. In the Eddas of the Scandinavians we find Odin walking by the seashore with his three brothers. Heaven and earth have been created, but there are as yet no human beings. The brothers come upon two trees. Instantly they hit upon the idea of changing them into a man and a woman. Each offering a contribution, one brother gives soul and life, the next wit and motion, and the third face, speech, sight, and hearing. Thus equipped the new creations move forward into history. It was as simple as that. And it was no more open to question than the Iranian account of how the first pair, rising from a rhubarb plant as a single unit, were divided into two by the grace of Ormuzd.

'Whence art thou?' inquires Penelope of the disguised Ulysses, 'for thou art not sprung of oak or rock, as old tales tell.' That wonderful tree, the ash, (my favourite, the companion of my vigils), which for so many centuries has held up its long lean fingers across the wintry way of man's pilgrimage, was not only the tree that in the eye of the Norsemen pillared the dome, but according to the Greeks it was the tree from which Zeus fashioned the bronze race of men. Thus also with the oak: the Romans saw the oaks as the first mothers of men, who fed their offspring on acorns. Can we not follow the unfolding thought? Men are so like trees — more so than any other creature. Men alone habitually preserve their perpendicular and raise their arms. A tree is stationary and has many arms and a big head — otherwise it almost resembles a human in a tight-fitting skirt. We still call our bodies, below the armpits, our *trunks*. We find nothing strange in the bold image of the man whose eyes had been opened by the power of Jesus — 'Lord, I see men as trees walking.'

There is no end to the figures and the fancies that became entwined with this theme. The Damaras of South Africa believed that the tree which they were pleased to call Omumborombonga was the progenitor of men, oxen, and zebras. Amongst the ancient legends of Ireland was the superstition that the first man was created from an alder tree and the first woman from a mountain ash, while a popular fairy-tale tells of a cow that went regularly and stood under an old hawthorn tree out of whose trunk a little wizened old woman came and milked her, and then went back into the tree again. As we have seen, trees could be of any proportion and in possession of boundless properties, sometimes hanging with fruits which were the size of elephants. From early days when the authors of the first book of the Mahâbhârata told of a gigantic fig tree from whose branches there hung devotees in human form, to the fourteenth century when an Italian traveller was assured by the natives of Malabar that they knew trees whose flowers consisted of pygmy men and women, we come across every sort of wild surmise — not stopping short of talking trees in Arabia that budded full-grown men and women. We are in those regions of the mind where in the riot of fancy anything is possible and all kinds of conceptions are mixed together, myth within myth, until we find that even the Flood that overwhelmed the earth was caused by a monkey which let loose a limitless lake upheld within the centre of a world-embracing tree, and that the two survivors of the deluge repopulated the world by sowing the seeds of the itma palm, which grew into human beings.

They were equally free to reverse the conception when they chose. They did not confine themselves to the idea that people sprang from trees; they also attended at the transformation of individuals into trees. Perhaps it would be truer to call it a poetical idea round which they were glad to weave many delightful stories in which certain trees took the place of men or gods or nymphs. This is particularly true of the Greeks and the Romans whose sad and happy legends conduct us into a world where men and gods and stars and earth come together so closely that the sun itself is but a chariot that can be driven across the meadows of the sky. They associated

the poplar with Phaeton, son of Helios, who rashly re-
quested that he might be allowed to drive the sun across
the heavens for one day; but not being strong enough to
control the rushing horses he was forced out of the
accustomed track and came so close to the earth as
nearly to set it on fire — thereupon Zeus killed him with
a flash of lightning and hurled him down into the river
Po. Witnessing his downfall, his sisters, who had yoked
the horses to the chariot, wept so bitterly that Zeus
changed them into poplars and their tears into amber.

There were many incidents of this kind. They associated the cypress with Cyparissos, the fair youth who
having killed his favourite stag, was so stricken that
Apollo in compassion changed him into a tree. They
associated the pine with the nymph, Pitys, who was cast
down from a cliff by Boreas, the jealous north wind.
They associated the almond with Phyllis, the Queen of
Thrace, who hanged herself in despair on being deserted
by the son of Theseus, and was changed into an almond
just as Melus, the priest of Aphrodite, having hanged
himself on receiving news of the death of Adonis, was
turned into an apple tree. They associated the myrrh
with Myrrha who, having gratified her passion for her
own father, and being then pursued by him with a
drawn sword, called upon the gods to render her invisible, who straightway transformed her into a myrrh
tree, and her tears into sweet-smelling resin: 'And still
she weeps, nor sheds her tears in vain, For still the
precious drops her name retain.'[1]

Just as the laurel is associated with Daphne who
suffered metamorphosis into that tree in order to escape
from Apollo, so was the lotis tree connected with Lotis
who had sought to avoid the embraces of Priapus; and

[1] Dryden.

later when her sister, Dryope, on passing the tree that had once been Lotis, plucked some fruit from it she at once found herself changing into another lotus tree, and though she screamed for pardon she saw that her feet had already become rooted to the ground. In the same way they associated the alder and the willow with two poor fishermen who on the Feast of Pales neglected her rites, with the result that as they stood on the bank of a stream they were fixed there by the outraged goddess, and saw their feet gaining roots in the water amongst the croaking frogs, and their arms becoming boughs, until they were wholly changed into alders and sad drooping willows. They associated the frankincense tree with Leukothea who was buried alive by her father for displacing Clythia in the affections of the Sun-god. They associated the pomegranate with Side who was changed into that tree after she had killed herself to escape the persecution of her father who had lost her mother.

Thus the legends grew and varied, sometimes in happier vein as when Baucis and Philomon, two worthy peasants, gave hospitality to Zeus and Hermes disguised as travellers (who had been turned from other cottage doors), and in recompense had their cottage turned into a temple with themselves as priest and priestess. And on hearing them pray that neither should witness the death of the other, the two gods devised a fitting finish to their lives. One day as they stood on the steps of the temple, tottering with age, they each saw the other's figure change and sprout with sudden verdure, and even as they kissed and said farewell they were each enclosed within a tree whose linking boughs ensured in death that their embrace would be eternal. This kind of idea found expression in many ages and in many climes. The broken-hearted Iseult, lying buried in the same church with

Tristram, was yet entwined with him by ivy which springing from each grave covered the distance between and met at the vaulted roof, there to cling together in a true lover's knot. The Chinese Emperor who wronged his secretary, Hampang, was defeated in the end. Failing to subdue Hampang's wife for whom he formed a violent passion, he threw the husband into prison where he died of grief. She then jumped from the roof — leaving a request to the king that she might be buried with her husband. The king paid no heed; but after the separate burial, overnight a cedar sprang from each grave, and within ten days they were able to link both their roots and branches, and thenceforth became known as the Cedars of Faithful Love.

## §XI FAMILY AND COMMUNITY TREES; SEX AND FERTILITY; MAYPOLE RITES; THE DARK SIDE OF TREE-WORSHIP

TREES that pillared the sky; men from trees and trees from men; trees that blessed and trees that cursed; trees that tempted, trees that taught — these did not exhaust the possibilities. We must proceed further.

They could be interwoven with the life of a person or a family or a community. The withering of such a tree was regarded as a catastrophe by those concerned. This kind of sentiment is, as we know, ingrained in our minds even to this day. Just as Sir Walter Scott planted acorns to judge by their success whether he would clear his debts, so when Lord Byron first visited his family seat at Newstead he planted an oak, and thereafter indulged the belief that his life and prosperity depended upon its fate. Every reader of Thomas Hardy will recall how, in *The Woodlanders*, John South feels convinced that he will die when the tree outside his window fails — and it is so. Of course in early days men went much further than this and took the matter with practical seriousness. It was a usual thing, especially among the Romans, to plant a tree at the birth of a son, and from its vigour to forecast the prosperity of the child. Such a tree was believed to be so bound up with the fate of the family that they watched over it with great anxiety, and we are told that the withering of the laurel grove of Augustus was held to portend the extinction of his line and the death of Nero, while the fall of Vespasian's cypress foretold the downfall of Domitian. The belief in such a connection with specially planted trees was so widespread that it is not surprising to learn from the Talmud that the destruction of Bithar in which four hundred thousand Israelites lost their lives, was caused by the resentment of a father whose precious tree had been wantonly destroyed by one of the inhabitants.

The idea of a Community Tree was just as important as the idea of a Family Tree. According to Mannhardt, there was scarcely an old German village without such a tree which was guarded with the greatest care: 'the I of the whole community' — devotions being paid to it and gifts placed on its branches. The ancient fig tree under which Romulus and Remus were found, was held to be so closely connected with the fortunes of the city, that when it began to show signs of decay the Romans were overcome with terror.

They could scarcely have felt this with such concern unless it had been connected in their minds with the idea of fertility and the idea of sex. Indeed the sexual aspect was highly complicated, and this does not seem to have been only one-sided. It appears that there was a certain idea of mutual benefit, in obedience to which naked men would go into certain plantations at night in order by a sort of sexual intercourse to fertilize them. I do not think that much is known definitely about this. Part of it is in the realm of speculation. And since speculation is only bearable when dealt with by deep and clear minds, let us go to Edward Carpenter for this. The tree was a most intimate presence to men, he writes in *Pagan and Christian Creeds*. 'It grew in the very midst of his Garden of Eden. It had a magical virtue, which his tentative science could only explain by chance analogies and assimilations. Attractive and beloved and worshipped by reason of its many gifts to mankind — its grateful shelter, its abounding fruit, its timber, and other valuable products — why should it not become the natural emblem of the female, to whom through sex man's worship is ever drawn? If the Snake has an unmistakable resemblance to the male organ in its active state, the foliage of the tree or bush is equally remindful of the female. What more clear than that the conjunction of Tree and Serpent is the fulfilment in nature of the sex-mystery which is so potent in the life of man and the animals? and that the magic ritual most obviously fitted to induce fertility in the tribe or the herds (or even the crops) is to set up an image of the Tree and the Serpent combined, and for all the tribe-folk in common to worship and pay it reverence. In the Bible with more or less veiled sexual significance we have this combination in the Eden-Garden and again in the brazen serpent and pole which Moses set up in the wilderness.'

That is the background against which we should see the meaning of the Maypole (and, for that matter, the Barber's Pole). In modern times some people still notice the approach of spring, and no attempts have been made, as yet, to produce an artificial one — though the

D 97

production of flowers out of season is welcomed. We do know when spring is coming, even in the town. We are conscious of it, and admit that it gives us quite a pleasant feeling; and until Mr. Eliot made that remark about April, it was still permissible for poets to do us an Ode to Spring. But it is scarcely possible for us to realize what it meant to men before the days of artificiality. It meant little less than a re-birth, a fresh start in life. Spirits rose and flowed over into rejoicing, shouting, singing, celebration. May the first became a signal for an exclamation of delight and relief and gratitude. The feeling was so deep, so intense, the comfort at the re-leafing was so religious, that for centuries and centuries the day was a day of worship; and it was not until 1644 that the Puritans, whose love of God was exceeded by their hatred of His creations, were powerful enough to put a stop to it and to forbid the rites accorded to 'that stinking idol' the Maypole.

This famous pole began as a tree which on May the first was brought into the village and erected there in order that the new-awakened energy of the forest might be communicated to the people; and as time went on and the pristine intention evolved into a pleasing annual ceremony, a Pole was set up which every year could be dressed with garlands and leaves into the semblance of a living tree. The general practices and evolvings of the idea in many countries and through many centuries provide a story which is not unfamiliar to us. It makes an appealing chapter in Greek, in German, and in English history — for in this matter the customs of ancient Greece and 'modern' Europe expose a remarkable similarity. The 'harvest-bush' of the Greeks with all its attendant activities at the Feast of Thorgelia bears an extraordinary resemblance to the 'harvest-May' of the

Western Germans who, selecting a green sapling at harvest-time, adorned it with flowers, ribbons, and coloured paper, and hung upon it fruit, eggs, cake, sausages, rings, needles, tobacco, and bottles of wine. As for the English ceremonies up to the days of Merry England, we need only turn to our Chaucer or Herrick to gather something of the exalted spirit of that long-lost gladness, and to see how when the god-venerating principle of the ceremonies had died down, that other godly principle, the amatory, rose up and licensed the revelry and the love-making.

In all cases there was the choice of a youth or a maiden who was called upon to personify the Spirit of Spring — the May Queen who is with us still. She carried with her a green bough, and it was once believed that through the bough and a representation of the god of vegetables, the genius of growth would beneficially affect the cows, the poultry and the fruit. In England the young people who had been up before sunrise to bring in the May, and had danced for hours upon the village green, completed the long day's celebration by crowning the May-Queen at sundown. But there was another ritual sometimes observed, especially in Germany — namely, the putting to death, in mimic form, this spirit of vegetation. Let us read one example of this from Frazer. 'In Lower Bavaria, the Whitsuntide representative of the tree-spirit — the Pfingstl, as he is called — was clad from top to toe in leaves and flowers. On his head he wore a high-pointed cap, the ends of which rested on his shoulders, only two holes being left for his eyes. The cap was covered with water-flowers and surmounted with a nosegay of peonies. The sleeves of his coat were also made of water-plants, and the rest of his body was enveloped in alder and hazel leaves. On each side of him marched a boy, holding up one of the Pfingstl's arms. These two boys carried drawn swords, and so did most of the others who formed the procession. They stopped at every house where they hoped to receive a present, and the people in hiding soused the leaf-clad boy with water. All rejoiced when he was well drenched. Finally he waded into the brook up to his middle, whereupon one of the boys, standing on the bridge, pretended to cut off his head.'

We may take this as another symbol of John Barley-corn who must be slain that he may rise again eternally. And if the god must die, why should not human sacrifices be made to him? We must remember the darker side of these things, even while we deplore the appalling Puri-tans. Human sacrifices *were* made to gods. That is the sort of fact we academically 'know' without realizing. It did happen. Early men did look out upon phenomena with fresh eyes, and without any kind of calm scientific approach. And they were terrified. We who talk of 'freedom from fear', what do we know of fear? We know nothing of fear, nothing of belief, nothing of wor-ship in comparison with them. They *believed in* their gods. There they were, a few yards off, ready to help or to punish. They must be placated somehow. Hence the whole paraphernalia of magic and sacrifice and wild screaming ritual dances. We who try to get 'a new stimulus' from primitive art, whose purpose was not art but magic; we who make a Hollywood holiday out of savages dancing madly round a fire, do not realize what these things once meant in terms of sheer reality. Glancing at a Maypole or a Barber's Pole (the origin of the latter which was associated with the medical practice of bleeding, going right back to the butcher-priest with his sacrificial post) we cannot conceive the deadly earnestness and the deadly fear that once lay behind them. We turn our minds, not as from something that really happened, but as from a nightmare, when we are faced with some of the early practices. Indeed when we think of the Grove of Upsala celebrating at the Vernal Equinox a great festival to the gods, at which six victims, one a man, the others dogs and horses, were sacrificed, and their bodies hung from the sacred trees; when we think of how, among the Kangra mountains of the Punjaub, a girl used to be annually sacrificed to an old cedar tree, the families of the village taking it in turn to supply the victim; when we think of the many primitive tribes that chose their most beautiful youth as a fitting representative to mount the steps of an altar and receive the plunging knife of the priest who then held up the still beating heart before the gaze of the multitude; when we think of the extravagant and fantastic scenes inaugurated in honour of the Mexican god Huitzilopochtli; of how thousands of human beings were sacrificed annually to him, their limbs being eaten by his worshippers; of how hundreds of new-born babies were placed one after another on the downward-sloping hand of the colossal god, from whence they slid into a furnace; of how even in 1486, when his temple was re-dedicated, seventy thousand people were killed — we revise any inclination we might have to idealize the wholly primitive days.

§ XII TREE CREDULITIES ABOUT MARRIAGE, MEDICINE AND HANGING

WE may turn with relief to the consideration of a few credulities concerning marriage, medical practice, and the virtue in hanging.

Trees were believed to exercise considerable influence upon marriage, with respect both to fertility and happiness. It was even thought to be a good thing to marry a tree as a preliminary to marrying a person. But first let us note that the marriages of trees themselves were frequently celebrated in the most elaborate manner, and when they were in blossom were treated as pregnant women so that no noise was made near them, and every man took off his hat in their presence. If a Hindoo had planted a grove of mangoes he could not eat its fruit until he had married it to some other tree, perhaps a tamarind. In view of the prestige attained by the owner according to the number of Brahmans who attended the ceremony, the expenses of such a marriage were considerable, and sometimes it was necessary for a family to sell all its gold and silver trinkets in order to marry a mango tree to a jasmine with due pomp and ceremony; and indeed it is known that the Rajah of Orchla at Ladhaura spent thirty thousand pounds upon the marriage ceremony of the holy basil to an ammonite fossil, for the hundred thousand guests who attended the rite had to be feasted, while the procession consisted of eight elephants, twelve hundred camels, and four thousand horses, all mounted and elegantly caparisoned.

The underlying belief in trees as promoters of fertility led to many curious practices. Krishna's marriage to the basil plant, that holder of the essence of Vishnu, is celebrated to the present day; and some tribes in the hill-country of India considered it expedient that before a bride or bridegroom were married they should both first go through a marriage ceremony to two trees, each clasping a trunk or being tied to it — the intention of this custom being to communicate to the betrothed the vigorous reproductive power of the tree. And after marriage trees were enlisted to ensure the bearing of children. Thus the sacred cedar of Gilgit, on the north-western frontier of India, was credited with the power of causing the herds to multiply and women to become pregnant. During the season of wheat sowing, three un-married youths who had been specially chosen and forced to undergo preliminary purification, visited the cedars on the mountains taking with them wine, oil, bread, and fruit. Having sprinkled the oil and wine onto a chosen tree, they performed a sacrificial feast. Returning to the village with a branch they placed it on a stone beside running water and sprinkled the blood of a goat upon it, while the rejoicing villagers danced round it. After this every man was free to go home bearing a spray of cedar. On his arrival he could say to his wife: 'If you want children, I have brought them to you; if you want cattle I have brought them; whatever you want I have it.'[1]

It seems that such an elaborate ritual was not required everywhere. A barren woman belonging to the Tahoe tribe of the Maoris had but to embrace a certain tree associated with the navel-strings of definite mythical ancestors, to be certain of receiving a child; amongst the Kara-Kirghiz it was deemed only necessary to roll on the ground beneath an apple tree to ensure conception; and in the town of Qua, near Old Calabar, there existed a palm which possessed such properties that if a barren woman ate one of its nuts she became a mother. Doubt-less some such belief lay behind the following Russian folk-tale celebrating a remedy for childless couples: the husband goes into the forest, cuts wood and makes a cradle; then his wife puts into it one of the logs he has cut, and begins swinging it, crooning the while a rune: 'Swing, blockie dear, swing!' After a little time the block

[1] FRAZER, *The Golden Bough*: The Magic Art, vol II, p. 50

begins to show a pair of legs, and the rejoicing woman swings the more until the block becomes a baby.

Trees might not only bring children. They could preserve love. This idea was widely held. The superstition in Slav countries, where it was believed that if two trees were planted before the houses of a newly wedded pair their happiness would last, found an equivalent in Prussia where it was believed that if a lover desired his sweetheart always to love him he could put three of her hairs into a fissure of a tree representing himself, and by this means ensure that her love would last with the life of the tree. Furthermore, some trees not only stimulated fertility and promoted happiness but also ensured easy delivery, so that we learn how women in Sweden and Africa, by virtue of clasping certain trunks in their arms or clothing themselves with the bark, were protected from danger and pain at the hour of childbirth. And this brings us to that aspect of tree-gifts to men which we may put under the head of medical practice.

So close seemed the relationship between man and other things, and so objective a disease, that it was thought that you could give it away like any other possession. Thus if you were giddy you could transfer your giddiness to a field by running naked round it. If you had warts, after going through a suitable ritual you could give them to the moon. Nothing offered more hospitality to ailments than trees. Just as you could make your lover continue to love you by locking some of her or his hair in the fissure of a tree, so you could get rid of fever by locking hair and nail-clippings in a tree-bole and then plugging it up. The best method of getting rid of gout was believed to be a frank approach to a fir tree when you would tie a knot in one of its twigs saying: 'God greet thee, noble fir. I bring thee my gout. Here will

I tie a knot and bind my gout into it.'[1] There were many ways of simply scraping off your disease, chief of which was that of passing through a cleft in a tree or a hole in a bush — a method which was especially effective with children, who also could be cured by being placed in a hole in a tree. Primitive dentistry provided similar methods and we may envy a remedy for toothache which was no more elaborate than that of scraping the tooth with a twig which was then plugged into a tree. The pain was thus transferred and would only return if the tree were cut down. In Africa medical practice was reserved for what were called devil trees upon which they hung all manner of articles touched by diseased persons, in order to transfer the malady. A piece of thread tied round the patient's neck and then hung onto a tree was considered by the Greeks and Romans sufficient to shift the illness, a remedy which was surely preferable to the French method of binding the sufferer to a trunk. Some races thought that ill luck as well as ordinary illness could safely be passed on in this way, and we find a custom amongst the Esthonians who handed over their bad luck to a tree by embracing it, walking three times round it at midnight, and taking a mouthful of the bark each time they encircled it.

It was also considered that it brought better luck to a dead man if he were buried on a tree than in the earth — whether by being placed in a box and stuck into the forks of branches, or simply strapped up. According to John Evelyn some nations carried this out with a view to honouring their more esteemed relations, since this position was nearer to heaven; and Sir John Mandeville, in describing his travels in India, spoke of a certain island where it was the custom to hang their

[1] *The Golden Bough*, vol. III. p. 28.

dead friends upon trees, 'and seyn that it is bettre, the Briddes that ben angels of God, eten hem, than the foule worms of the Erthe'.

There is some connection here, I suppose, with the curious idea that hanging from a tree was considered to have occult significance of a positive kind, and that swinging from a tree brought purification to the swinger. Odin was the god of the hanged as well as a tree-god. All sacrifices to him were made by honourable hanging. His horse is said to have been a name for the gallows. From this springs the origin of 'a piece of rope' as conferring good luck upon the recipient, just as the drops of blood from the hanged were regarded as particularly potent fertilizers. Pliny, after speaking of the bit of rope as a sovereign cure for headaches — which no hanged man would deny — added that the hairs of the hanged were a febrifuge. John O'Neill draws attention to the account of the plain of Circe in the *Argonautika* where rows of osiers and willows were growing, on whose branches dead men hung, since the Colchians abominated either burning or burying their men — though women, unlike the men who had died in their beds, were never granted the privilege of being hanged after death.

This unfairness, however, seems to have been made good by the existence of certain trees which possessed the power to stimulate women to hang themselves before death. Chaucer tells a tale taken from Cicero which runs to the following effect. A man by the name of Paletinus, in a great state of agitation one day, called his son and his neighbours around him and said: 'Alas! A fatal tree is growing in my garden. My first poor wife hanged herself upon it; then my second; and now my third. Truly I have cause for lamentation!' Hearing this, a neighbour called Arrius made answer: 'I am surprised that you should think fit to weep at so unusual an instance of good fortune. If you will be kind enough to give me a few cuttings from this admirable tree, I will be happy to divide them with my neighbours, and thereby give every man a chance to indulge this laudable aim of his spouse.' Paletinus, being a man with an eye to business, complied with his friend's suggestion; and in due course found that this remarkable tree was the most productive part of his estate.

## § XIII THE POWER OF TREES IN ALL AGES

No doubt many of the facts rehearsed in the above sections are surprising enough in our eyes. Yet we are not surprised. Trees still have such an effect upon us (if unconsciously), that nothing concerning man in his relation to them strikes us as wholly strange. We still pay a certain homage to the mystery of the tree, the branch, the leaf. We still set up a fir as a Christmas Tree every year, which perhaps even yet is not wholly spoilt by the fantasia of commercialism that surrounds it. We carry on this bit of tree-worship instead of the May-pole. Its origin, of course, lies very far away. It has been traced back to the Yggdrasil Ash, and the lights with which we deck it now were once the stars that shone within the branches of the mighty Tree that held up heaven on its crown. It seems to have had, as one parent, a tree that blossomed suddenly just before the New Year. Such a tree would naturally make a great impression. Thus the pedigree of the Christmas Tree — with its lights, its artificial flowers, its apples and so on — links with the legends of the Christmas flowering-trees which was a familiar theme of the Middle Ages, the chief example being the Glastonbury Thorn that became such an object of veneration that the merchants of Bristol found the export of its blossoms a remunerative business. This is a field of inquiry which makes a mythologist's holiday, though I get left behind. The reader will be happy in the hands of O'Neill who clears up the matter a bit more: 'Professor G. Schlegel cites from Maurer an Icelandic legend that the Reynir (Rowan) covers itself on Christmas-*night* with lights which the strongest wind cannot put out. These night-lights are, of course, initially, the stars on the branches of the Universe Tree. He also extracts from Wanglang's *Antiquities of Thsin* the statement that in the Chinese state of Thsin, previously to 247 B.C., a tree with a hundred flowers and lamps was placed on New-year's night at the step of the audience-hall, while outside the correct gate candles of five and of three feet were lit'.[1]

One way or another the Christmas Tree came into recognized existence and evolved into what we have today — though curiously enough it does not seem to have reached England till the Prince Consort took it from Germany in the last century. The ministers of the Christian religion were able to incorporate it into their devotions on the ground that Adam and Eve had something to do with it. It was customary for the Church in early times to devote the day before Christmas to the memory of Adam and Eve and to give a dramatic presentation of the story of the Creation and Fall in connection with the Nativity — in which of course a tree played a prominent part. The legend that the cross of Christ was made from a slip of the Tree of Know-

[1] JOHN O'NEILL, *The Night of the Gods*.

ledge served as a link and made the display of some tree
an essential element in the celebrations.

Thus we have it with us still. We still hang up holly
and ivy and other leaf decorations in our houses on
Christmas Day — a practice which originated with the
idea that a home would thus be given to the elves who
had nowhere to go when the leaves fell from the trees
in winter. We still hang up a branch of mistletoe — a
practice which carries us back to the Druids whose
custom it was in the winter to place it upon their altars
in the belief that the Spirit of the Wood retreated there
when the rest of the leaves had fallen. We are still
ready to roll out the Yule Log or Yule Clog as the
specialist, Brand, called it (he would) — a custom which
links us with the days when fires were lit at the Winter
Solstice to celebrate the return journey of the sun.

How eager we remain to find in trees some occult
power to save or to bless! Thy rod and thy staff, they
comfort me — the very words bring comfort. The
conductor must have his baton. The conjurer must have
his wand. When we search for water we like to use wood
for our divining rod. When we desire to make a gesture
of peace it is the olive branch we offer. When we would
honour the poet we speak of conferring upon him the
laurel and the bays. And who does not see the symbol
of all human suffering in that crown of thorns placed
upon the head of him who was nailed to the bitter wood
and lifted up on the cross for the derision of the city
before going down among the dead?

We cannot overestimate the influence which trees
have exerted over the minds and the works of men. From
the cylinders of Chaldea to the aisles and the window-
tracery of our cathedrals, that influence is written. If,
after having been to a museum and examined the extra-

ordinary and rather frightening Chaldean symbols of tree-worship of 4000 B.C., we then enter the Christian medieval edifice of St. Mark's at Venice, we will see embedded in the walls a number of sculptured slabs on each of which a conventionalized plant, with foliage rendered in truthful detail, is set between two fabulous monsters, the whole making a design which can be traced back to the signs and symbols of tree-worship as exhibited four to six thousand years ago by the Chaldean Semites. And who will deny that we in the West have carried the forest into the architecture of the cathedral? The peace and the mystery, the soft encircling silence of the glades, the holy calm within the vaulted tree-walled path, these we find again when we enter the Gothic Church and pace the aisles therein and gaze upon the fluted trunk-like pillars and look up at the fretted branches of the roof. It is no accident that the very German historian, Spengler, says in *The Decline of the West*: 'The character of the Faustian Cathedral is that of the *forest*.' He saw in the mighty elevation of the nave above the flanking aisles, in the transformation of the columns into pillars and clustered-pillars that grow up out of the earth and spread on high into an infinite subdivision and interlacing of lines and branches — 'the architectural actualizing of a world-feeling that had found the first of all its symbols in the high forests of the Northern plains, the deciduous forest with its mysterious tracery, its whispering and ever-mobile foliage over men's heads, its branches straining through the trunks to be free of earth.'

We have no forests in England now — only woods. We have plenty of elm-tree tracery. That is good enough. In the setting of its hieroglyphics scriptured against the cold winter sunset, we have an illuminated manuscript, a window opening on infinity.

THAT brings me to the end of this sketch concerning
the mythology of trees. I have used the past tense
practically throughout. Sometimes it should have been
the present tense — for some of the practices are still
performed. And I am not blind to the fact that a formidable body of fascinating examples could be given of up-
to-date tree-worship in out-of-date places. Yet obviously
the theme belongs to the past, and even where practised
can have little of the deadly earnestness and fear
behind it as in earlier times. Thus I have treated
that climate of thought as past.

But before closing I would like to remind myself and
you that there still exist primitive races living in enormous forests that are quite untamed and largely un-
explored by man. It would be fitting to close with the
song of the Mambuti hunters who live on the edge of the
great Ituri Forest in Africa. After the extremities and
fantasias which we have been examining, and before we
pass to a consideration of our modern attitude towards
trees in terms of goods and money, it may help to give
balance if we listen to the words of the reverential but
not foolish nor frantic Mambuti. This is the song the
Chief Musician sings:

Forest!
Thou art beautiful and always green and fresh and
    young.
As beautiful and green and young as a virgin
That Muungu, the God of Gods, hath made.
Hath he, himself, made.

Forest
Thou art a mother to us, thine own children.
A mother who giveth us food and drink and shelter
And weapons and medicines and all.
Who giveth us life and strength, and death and weakness, too.
Who giveth all.

A mother to us, thou art.
As thou hast been to our fathers.
And to the fathers of the fathers of our fathers. For ever.
As thou wilt be to our sons.
And to the sons of the sons of our sons.  For ever.

Mother Forest!
Thou art great.  How can I say how greatly great thou art?
I, and my wives and my little ones, walk toward where the sun rises.
We tire, we sleep, we eat, we walk in the path.  Again and again.
But never see the end of thee.

I, and some other daring youths, go on this side and that side,
As far as the Okwapi goes, and the Sori, and the Ngurube.
Their tracks we follow until the breath leaves our mouths
Until we come where the evil spirits dwell,
But do we ever see the end of thee?

Oh, Great Mother Forest![1]

[1] COMMANDER GATTI, *Great Mother Forest.*

# BIBLIOGRAPHY

*In particular*:

FRAZER, J. G., *The Golden Bough*
PHILPOT, J. H., *The Sacred Tree*
PORTEOUS, A., *Forest Folklore*
CARPENTER, E., *Christian and Pagan Creeds*
RENDELL HARRIS, *The Ascent of Olympus*
O'NEILL, J., *The Night of the Gods*
ROBERTSON SMITH, *The Religion of the Semites*


*General*:

SPENGLER, O., *The Decline of the West*
WILDE, LADY, *Ancient Legends of Ireland*
HUMBOLDT, A. V., *Examen Critique*
HESIOD, *Works and Days*
HERODOTUS, Curry's Trans., Book VI.
TACITUS, *The History*
HOMER, *The Odyssey*
OVID, *Metamorphoses*
VIRGIL, *The Aeneid*
PLINY, *Natural History*
SENECA, *Epistles*
DICKINSON, L., *The Greek Idea*
FARNELL, L. R., *The Cults of the Greek States*
LANG, A., *Myth, Ritual, and Religion*
TYLOR, E. B., *Early History of Mankind*
     ,,      *Primitive Culture*
MASPERO, G., *The Dawn of Civilisation*
GALTON, F., *Narrative of an Explorer*
SKEAT, W. W., *Malay Magic*
KEARY, G. F., *The Vikings of Western Christendom*
GREY, G., *Polynesian Mythology*

# BIBLIOGRAPHY

KEIGHTLEY, J., *Fairy Mythology*
      ,,        *Classical Mythology*
GOBLET D'ALVILLA, *The Migration of Symbols*
MANNHARDT, K., *Der Baumkultus der Germanen, etc.*
GRIMM, J., *Teutonic Myth*
BARING-GOULD, S., *Curious Myths of the Middle Ages*
WYATT GILL, W., *Myths and Songs from South Pacific*
FOLKARD, R., *Plant Lore, Legends and Lyrics*
DE GUBERNATIS, *Mythologie des Plantes*
BOTTICHER, C., *Der Baumkultus der Hellenen*
STANLEY, H. W., *In Darkest Africa*
COOK, W. A., *Through the Wilderness of Brazil*
BATES, H. W., *The Naturalist on the Amazons*
MAXWELL, G., *In Malay Forests*
RINDER, F., *Old World Japan*
KINGSLEY, M., *Travels in West Africa*
WEEKS, J. H., *Among the Congo Cannibals*
WILSON, J. L., *West Africa*
TOMLINSON, H. M., *The Sea and the Jungle*
GATTI, COMMANDER, *Great Mother Forest*
RALSTON, J., *Russian Folk Tales*
MURRAY-GILBERT, *Four Stages of Greek Religion*

# PART THREE

# THE TRANSITION

# THE TRANSITION

THEN the gods died. Pan perished. Later he was to return as Pantheism; but in the meanwhile he and all his crew were withdrawn from their earthly tenements and held no more traffic amongst men.

The old conception of plurality became worn out, being at last too much of a strain upon belief. The idea began to gain ground that there was only one god and that he was not attached to the earth, and neither subject to view nor interview. This new conception had the vitality of freshness and might have served as well as the old idea if all the races of mankind could have agreed upon the identity of this single god. Unfortunately there were disputes over him, one race projecting one favourite and another claiming quite a different person — each candidate being conceived as extremely jealous of his god-head. The resulting clashes between them make by no means the happiest chapters in the history of religion. It is a cheering thought that at least we can claim to have reached better days on this score, now that it is recognized that neither monotheism nor polytheism touch the core of religion, which is a mystic experience of the Divine and therefore faith in it.

What concerns us here in the change from the first idea to the second, is that whereas under polytheism the gods were intimately connected with the earth, and stimulated veneration for it, under monotheism deity was extracted from the earth. God was promoted to higher regions. He went completely out of sight. It became possible to fear God without fearing Nature — nay, to love God (whatever was meant) and to hate his creations.

This attitude reached its climax with what is called Puritanism. In the history of mankind there is nothing more shameful than the spectacle of human beings perspiring with religious fervour and at the same time turning away with horror and loathing from a fresh green leaf or a naked body. That frenzy passed. Then the deity began to be secretly hated. But this did not mean the restoration of the gods and a renewal of respect for the creation. Science came in and began to 'conquer' nature. The gods were dead, and god was dead: into what channel now would energy flow? Into the exploitation of the earth. All respect for every living thing was abandoned; the Golden Bough was turned into boughs of gold; the once god-informed trees became 'timber'; and the way was made straight for the princes of industry and the kings of commerce.

The above is merely a statement of the transition. The history of the transition would be obliged to take into account the untidy nature of change. The gods did not die all at once, nor quickly. It took time to get rid of them. In vain did the Hebrew Prophets denounce the Groves; in vain did Mahomet put tree-priests to death for honouring acacias. The worship died hard. The ecclesiastical records of the Councils of Agde, Auxerre and Nantes were forced to make prohibitions against sacred trees and woods, and to treat as insane those who burnt candles in honour of trees. These records, says John O'Neill, 'give us an all-powerful motive for the almost cosmic crime of the fatal destruction of the European forests'. That and cupidity. The usual mixture of motives. If trees militate against the worship of the god above, destroy them; if trees are not venerable then use them for money-making.

It will be my task now to consider how we stand today

after some centuries of the new attitude towards the earth introduced by monotheism and carried forward by commercialism allied with science. Sorry if this Part is rather short. I see no necessity to write a hundred pages marking the transition — always supposing that I possessed the qualifications for doing so. But no candid person, with some knowledge of the past, and with his eyes open today will deny the broad truth of my statement. And what concerns us is not the process of change but the fact, and our present position as a result of it.

The result has been bad, as we shall see — and indeed as everyone knows. But if we retrieve the situation we shall be in a happier position than we have ever been before. Tree-worship, as we have seen, evolved from crude forms into the general idea that they were the guardians of fertility. There was profound truth in that. Unfortunately the truth was seen in a false light. The trees were thought to be alive in the wrong way — to be gods or the habitation of gods. Thus when people no longer believed in these deities, the trees ceased to call for veneration or care. We are gainers, if having passed through that stage, we now enter an era when respect for the earth is being reborn, and science, no longer speaking in terms of conquest, can inform us with a deeper truth why trees really are the guardians of fertility.

# PART FOUR

# THE REVENGES OF NATURE

# CHAPTER I

# THE GOVERNMENT OF NATURE AND THE MINISTRY OF TREES

## §1 THE EQUILIBRIUM OF THE PRIMAL ORDER

BEFORE going a step further let us take a firm grasp of the obvious and remind ourselves of something too easily forgotten. We must remember that man is a late arrival on the scene of natural operations. It is not his fault that he has come; he did not ask to be born; and his birth is the strangest thing that ever happened. It was so unnatural. There seems to be inherent wisdom in the workings of nature. In this instance that wisdom is hard to discern. It is as if a bird had laid a bomb instead of an egg.

No one has been able to explain this. Let us not try. Rather let us contemplate for a few minutes the Order of Nature without reference to man. Is there an Order, is there really any Natural Order? Well, the opposite to order is chaos, and the universe is remarkably coherent. There is government throughout.

We have just passed through a short phase when the public has been slightly bewildered by scientific men who happened to be rather weak thinkers, amusing themselves by comparing organisms with engines as if there were no difference between a pistil and a piston; by confusing description with explanation; by declaring that the universe is a chaos of conflicting atoms; and by failing to observe that when they insisted that everything is governed by chance they had thereby acknowledged that it is — *governed*. The idea of Purpose or lack of it was introduced into all this. Grave questions were asked and elaborate volumes written on this question of purpose, as if the movements of molecules could determine it. What was really being asked was — Is there any point in life? This question can only be answered emotionally. The universe is given and makes a total impression: we value it according to our psychology. Any man is entitled to say that he hates it. For myself, I like it, or a lot of it. My appreciation of it cannot be undermined by any description of its operations nor by the suggestion that in so many million years the sun may cool and go out. I applaud its existence whether it lasts for ever or comes to an end one day, whether it is run by atoms or by a god on a throne somewhere. A purely personal reaction, subject to my psychology. But what is not subject to psychology, what also cannot be altered by any talk about 'conflicting atoms', is the fact that the finished article, the universe, is unified, is governed, is lawful.

What are we saying when we speak of the Order of Nature? We are saying that the unnumbered phenomena that we see existing in an intricate complex maintain a marvellous degree of order and balance. They melt into one another. They are one another. A cow standing there in the field with its huge wet nose, looks singular enough. But where does the substance of that heavy piece of flesh it carries, come from? The cow is not created out of nothing, it is not really on its own, it is simply part of the universe, a moving part. There is the field: it happens to be stationary. The cow moves about, but it is part of the field, and is continually recruited from the field. It cannot move, it cannot grow unless it takes in a portion of the field. This is called eating. If it fails to do so, then it will stop in its path, and will sink back into the field. This is called dying. Now, it is in a high degree undesirable and useless to fall into the pit of speculation and ask Who contrived this? or to explain it in any way: these are questions we must always pass over while doing our best to describe it and fully realize it. Having done so, having laid hold on the obvious before our eyes, we can pass to less visible types of the heavenly pomp. Take the case of the fish, the snail, and the plant for instance.

Place a bowl of water where the sun can strike it, and put a snail, a fish, and a water-plant into it. The population of three in this cosmos will thrive for months by virtue of mutual exchange. The fish lives on the plant. The waste of the fish is prepared by the snail so that it can be manufactured by the plant which uses the waste of both fish and snail for its own purposes, and in so doing releases oxygen that purifies the water and guards the animals from suffocating. When the physical and chemical equilibrium is thus maintained by the action of different creatures, we get what ecologists call a balanced environment. Remove the snail, and the plant will droop and the fish will fail. Remove the fish, and there can be no further exchange between the plant and the snail. Remove the plant, and neither fish nor snail can pasture. It looks like three in one and one in three. But of course it is more than that. We must not forget the water. We must not forget the sun. Take their action away from the fish, the plant, and the snail, and again this cosmos will totter to its foundations.

What are we saying by virtue of the above illustration? Only the obvious — that when things are in their right place they are all right. But are they not inevitably in their right place? The Order of Nature either is an order or it is not, and everything must be in its proper environment. Nothing could ever start in an improper environment, otherwise it would never start: the bloc only breaks into many organisms when the conditions are favourable — (at least such is my vision of the matter). Thus when we speak of the Order of Nature are we not saying something as obvious as that the sun rises and sets with marked punctuality? Yes, I think that that is really all we are saying — that the universe works, that it does not break down. There is an inherent principle at work which ensures a balance.

I am happy to make that elephantine truism. There is a fiction that people fight shy of original ideas. It is supposed that you cannot get original ideas into people's heads. This is untrue — we love a new idea to play with. What we cannot get into our heads is a platitude, a truism. Let us get this one in — that nature does preserve an equilibrium. And then let us accept the fact that this does not rule out *calamity* for individual units or even whole species if the Order at any time is overbalanced. Occasional calamity for individuals is part of the Order.

Thus we do not find one species becoming predominate over the rest. It is not possible for any species to achieve this. About three-quarters of a million species of insects have already been identified and therefore named.[1] A single pair of plant lice, it is said, could produce enough progeny to outweigh the human population of the world fivefold. In six months flies can raise six trillion offspring. We have all seen what a plague of caterpillars can do to a wood within a month. We have

[1] According to Macneile Dixon 'there are not less than ten million varieties of insect'.

all heard what happens when a cloud of locusts appears. The Australians know a little about rabbits under this head. The white ants in massed millions have sometimes more power than an earthquake. How is it that a balance is preserved between all these creatures, and that one lot does not empire it above all the others? This is what all units attempt to do. But when they succeed too well their food gives out and the conditions in which they normally thrive are changed. In nature nothing fails like excess. And normally the balance is held by virtue of each succumbing to enemies which keep them down. Thus birds pay insects great attention. It is estimated that in the U.S.A. three billion breeding birds are insectivorous. The proud cockroach whose line is linked with ancestors before the first forests of the world, and whose digestive system can easily assimilate 'a mustard plaster, an Egyptian mummy, or Jefferson's *Manual on the Constitution*,'[1] is itself readily digested by a variety of birds. During the fledgling period the starling feeds insects to its young at the rate of up to three hundred and fifty visits a day, while the ordinary house-wren brings back an insect every two minutes. It gives us an insight into the resistance which nature offers these tiny creatures when we learn that the potato-beetle is attacked by twenty-five species of birds, the alfalfa weevil by forty-five, the coddling-moth by thirty-six, the gipsy-moth by forty-six, house-flies by forty-nine, bill-bugs by sixty-seven, cut-worms by ninety-eight, leaf-hoppers by one hundred and twenty, and wire-worms by one hundred and sixty-eight. Nor are birds their only enemies: the bat and the shrew, the mole and the squirrel, the armadillo, the badger and the skunk are also fond of insects. But should these rodents

[1] See STUART CHASE, *Rich Land, Poor Land.*

thrive too well thereon, they in turn are looked after by the birds. The various owls like nothing better than rats, mice, shrews, voles, and rabbits. When in 1907 a plague of field-mice invaded the region of the Humboldt River in Nevada, gulls, hawks, and owls came on the scene, and in one month had disposed of one hundred thousand mice.

It is difficult to visualize the amount of creatures, big or small, that exist in the world. Could one member of each species pass before our eyes as in parade it would take some time before the show was over. Would we then, gasping at such numbers and such variety, wonder how they could all get on together? Or is that the right word? Have they developed the faculty of living together? When the 100,000 mice fell before the gulls, the hawks, and the owls, was that not failure to live in unity? In speaking of the order of nature, are we not merely exchanging a happier phrase for 'nature red in tooth and claw'? When, under days of frightful frost and ice, there is a huge, silent massacre of birds, what right have we to speak of nature as well ordered from the point of view of the birds? To this we must reply, I think, that the redness of nature's tooth and claw is part of the order; and that the word Order cannot be equated with Painlessness, but rather with the Basis-for-existence. Again we are bound to acknowledge that our reaction to existence on such a basis, is a matter of temperament. We should invite the birds to take a metaphysical view of the matter and to remind themselves that only appearances are against them, and to sing with Emerson: 'If the red slayer thinks he slays, And if the slain thinks he is slain, They know not well the subtle ways I keep and pass and turn again.' We are foolish if we try to do without philosophy in this world. We should always bear in mind the words of that unprofessional philosopher, Anton Chekov: 'So long as a man likes the splashing of a fish he is a poet. But when he knows that the splashing is nothing but the chase of the weak by the strong, he is a thinker; but when he does not understand what sense there is in the chase, or what use in the equilibrium which results from destruction, he is becoming silly and dull as he was when a child. And the more he knows and thinks the sillier he becomes.'

Silly? Can Chekov be allowed to sweep aside heavy-weight philosophers in a single phrase? I don't see why not. Yet I would hesitate to use the word myself. For there are passages even in Macneile Dixon's tremendous book *The Human Situation* which might thus come under that head. He writes: 'How difficult to recognize in the ferocities we see around us the subtle power which made the brain, which elaborated with consummate exactness the mechanism of the heart and lungs, all the devices by which the body maintains its existence! That nature should create a world full of difficulties and dangers, and thereupon proceed to place within it fabrics of an infinite delicacy and complexity to meet these very dangers and difficulties is a contradiction that baffles the understanding. With a cunning past all human thought she solves the problems she has, as it were, absent-mindedly set herself. The flood and the earth-quake have no consideration for the plant or animal, yet nature which sends the flood and earthquake has provided, with foresight or in a dream, for the living things they destroy. She both smiles and frowns upon her own creation, and is at once friendly and unfriendly. Like a scarlet thread it runs through her dominion, this inconsistency. Side by side with the undeniable and admirable adjustment between things organic and inorganic, you have the hostility, the discordance. What wonder that men, bewildered by this inexplicable procedure, have supposed her governments distributed amongst a hierarchy of squabbling deities, persecuting or protecting this or that race of men — Zeus for the Greeks, Jehovah the Jews. What wonder they supposed even the trees to be the better of protecting deities, the olive Athena, the vine Dionysus? Ah, nature! subtle beyond all human subtlety, enigmatic, profound, life-giver and life-destroyer, nourishing mother and assassin, inspirer of all that is best and most beautiful, of all that is most hideous and forbidding.'

Thus the author of that great book — *The Human Situation* — himself extracts a deity, as it were, an outside organizer, calling it 'she' or 'nature'. Need we make that approach? How would it be if we do not postulate an outside organizer of the whole in that manner — but take as given an inexplicable growth? We would be no worse off. Dixon is not pleased with our tendency to speak in terms of unity and wholeness. 'That the world is a unity,' he continues, 'the philosophers and men of science reiterate with wearisome persistence. That it is united they have the sense not to proclaim. How the world became disunited they have not told us.' Certainly these are words to make us think again. Yet what is he saying? That the units are not linked in fraternal embrace — not that they are disunited. But everything goes to show that they are linked, they do form a whole. Yet what of it, it may be asked, if that whole is not to our liking? It is a fair question. For there is nothing necessarily meritorious in unity if the article is unpleasant. We are entitled to reject it utterly if we consider that there is too much room for improvement. But on the whole men do not reject it. Quite the contrary.

And Dixon, who always faces all the facts, is careful to acknowledge this before closing his chapter.

Our immediate concern here is with the equilibrium which results from the complex of laws and forces. The reader knows that the few illustrations which I have given above, are as a thimbleful out of the lake of known facts concerning the interactions and pleasing exchanges of natural life, and that the known facts are as a thimbleful out of the ocean of what is still unknown. But we have enough to go on, we know that there is a balance, that order is held finally amongst phenomena however often and no matter upon what scale temporary disorder may break out. The Order of Nature should be a more fruitful conception than the Survival of the Fittest. The latter phrase — contrary to Darwin's intention — conveys merely that those survive who do survive, or that the strongest survive. Up till very recently it has been assumed that man offered proof that the strongest could survive — no matter how much he expanded, or how much he disturbed the scheme with his tools and his guns and his insecticides and all the rest of it. That was the famous 'conquest of nature' — which is beginning to look a bit thin now.

## §II THE RULE OF RETURN

WE have just glanced at the best-known and seldom forgotten aspect of the wheel of life — the way in which each creature receives others into itself and gives itself to others. Man appreciates one side of this anyway — the receiving of others into himself; though he so rarely holds to his side of the bargain by giving himself to others that it is regarded as an event when anyone is eaten.

This brings us to another very important aspect of the Order — namely, the ever-active movement of return. All these creatures of the earth whose numbers could never be counted, are, as it were, motor crops. They come out of the earth, and when they die they do so by either entering into the bowels of others or into the bowels of the earth — in both cases giving further vitality to the devourer. They come into the world and they receive the gifts of the world, its air and water and soil: this is called growing. In due course they give it all back, all of it. Some ecologists say that they give back a fraction more than they receive. This may be so. If it is, then the world is adding to itself, increasing itself. Yet this seems unlikely. I do not see how there can be such a thing as total addition or multiplication. It is more likely that there has always been and will always be the same amount of substance: yesterday the world a flaming ball, today changed into earth, air, and water: nothing added, nothing subtracted, all conserved. A question of change, not of addition. Indeed I have little doubt that the learned could point out to me that if the totality could grow as its units grow, we would very soon notice it; and I suppose that the law of the Conservation of Energy carries in itself a denial of total Addition. So I beg leave to question the soundness of any ecologist who suggests that when any living creature dies and renders its account, it is in a position to give more than it has received.

The main thing, however, is that it does return what it has received, not only in terms of a corpse, but also when it is alive. When it receives another creature into itself, when it eats that creature, it can only use a portion of it and must pass out from its body the remainder. We call it waste or excreta. But of course waste is an absolute misnomer. It is no more waste than a corpse, and can be devoured by certain other creatures and by the earth itself. The creatures in the natural order do not think of it as waste, they do not think of it at all, they just return it haphazard to the earth. This goes on day after day, year after year, century after century, countless tons of excreta being returned to the earth. To the earth: not to the sky, nor to the sea. The amount of this, for one single day, if assembled in a heap would stagger the beholder.

This unbroken circuit of return of good received, provides one of the most glaring aspects of the Order. And how we step outside it! I am not ready yet to speak at any length of Man in relation to the Natural Scheme; but it is proper to remind ourselves at this point of what is perhaps the most civilized of all things concerning him. He does not hesitate to receive into himself as many creatures as possible (no animal in fact approaches him in this), and he also can use only part of them, and must chemically treat the remainder and pass it on. But towards this matter passed out he has an attitude all his own. Wherever he dwells there is found a private little place called a *closet* or w.c. by means of which he can keep the product almost invisible from himself, and be means of pipes can keep it totally invisible from others. These pipes and underground passages, which he calls his sewerage system, are designed so as to prevent any of this product, which he calls waste, from reaching the soil. It reaches the sea and the rivers: 'in England we waste every year 219,000 tons of nitrogen, 55,000 tons of phosphate and 55,000 tons of potash as sewage sludge and house refuse that pollute the rivers and are lost in the sea'.[1] Europe and the United States combined,

[1] H. J. MASSINGHAM, *The Tree of Life.*

133

dispose of 20 million tons of nitrogen, potassium, and phosphorus every year in this way. The stuff is not lost, of course; it remains in the world, but in the ocean — that is in the wrong place for the good of earth.

This subject is painful indeed: we are right to draw back from it — for the quality of what we pass out, its smell, is such a terrible comment upon our physical corruption in comparison with the animals. We are right to feel ashamed and wish to hide our product, when we witness the bowel action of a horse: the easy delivery, the sudden ending, and the clean flesh at the finish . . . What a far cry it is from the coral reefs which are the excreta of polyps, to the sewers of London and Paris! How strange that the first should proceed from the lowliest of all the children of the world, and the second from ourselves who claim to be the highest.

## §III  THE NATURAL CREATION AND RENEWAL OF SOIL

WE have looked from our window at one aspect of the dance — the circuit of the creatures. But the wheel includes the earth upon which they dwell: the balance is also between air, water, soil, and plant.

The earth was once chiefly rock. If we wish to face the foundation of life and to gaze upon the mystery of the first floor, we must look at a rock. It seems steady. It appears lasting. But it is passing away. It cannot face the scrutiny of Time. For it is being weathered by wind and water, and Time is but the tool of Motion which is eternal. Fractions of stone fell, and falling laid the foundations of a soil. If that one poor figure is felt to be inadequate to describe the history of nature covering many millions of years, we cannot help it — perhaps the bare fact is good enough.

A rocky pile in modern times may take a long time to vanish; but there were periods of acceleration of the process by means of volcanoes, earthquakes, ice ages, and excessive violence of storm. The fact remains that under the rule of movement a portion of the rocks was turned into a substance ready to receive the first forms of verdure. I shall permit myself to write *turn into* verdure, since it seems more sensible to say that than to say it received something which was not there. A few more million years roll on and we see the masses of carboniferous forests. Everyone knows, whether vaguely or in detail, the rest of the story. We have just glanced at the Order of Nature governing the life and death of the creatures who dwelt and dwell among the plants. How about the soil itself?

Let us rehearse the well-known facts in a brief paragraph. Since soil starts as rock it naturally contains mineral properties. I need not enumerate them here, but we should remember that nitrogen, phosphorus, and potassium are three of the most important since they make the growth of plants possible. In fact plants rose from them, or they turned themselves into plants, and anyway still feed plants. Airy substances! most delicate and light! We can see how easily they could be washed away. How complex is this stuff we call soil! an amazing integration of those chemical properties, of the rock particles, of the plant ashes, of insects amounting to millions per acre, of quite countless bacteria — no wonder we cannot make an inch of this material ourselves! We call it simply — humus. Obviously it is highly vulnerable. But in the Natural Order it does not suffer harm. The tempest breaks out, the wind whips the earth, the torrent falls; but the foundations of the house of life are neither blown nor washed away. For the soil has fostered those who foster it. It is nailed down by grass. It is pegged down by trees.

This does not mean that there is no destruction. There is destruction. There is natural destruction — or erosion. That is to say there is renewal. The scientific term is denudation. The process is described with such admirable clarity by Mr. G. V. Jacks that it would be a pity not to quote his words. 'What is usually known as "geological erosion" or "denudation" is a universal phenomenon which through thousands of years has carved the earth into its present shape. Denudation is an early and important process in soil formation, whereby the original rock material is continually broken down and sorted out by wind and water until it becomes suitable for colonization by plants. Plants, by the binding effect of their roots, by the protection they afford against rain and wind and by the fertility they impart to the soil, bring denudation almost to a standstill. Everyone must have compared the rugged and irregular shape of bare mountain peaks where denudation is still active with the smooth and harmonious curves of slopes that have long been protected by a mantle of vegetation. Nevertheless, some slight denudation is always occurring. As each superficial film of plant-covered soil becomes exhausted it is removed by rain or wind, to be deposited mainly in the rivers and sea, and a corresponding thin layer of new soil forms by slow weathering of the underlying rock. The earth is continually discarding its old, worn-out skin and renewing a sheath of soil from the dead rock beneath. In this way an equilibrium is reached between denudation and soil formation so that, unless the equilibrium is disturbed, a mature soil preserves a more or less constant depth and character indefinitely. The depth is sometimes only a few inches, occasionally several feet, but within it lies the whole capacity of the earth to produce life. Below that thin layer comprising the delicate organism known as soil is a planet as lifeless as the moon.'[1]

The only difficulty about the above is in the last sentence. Personally I am no believer in these vast gaps. Still, it doesn't matter here. We need not fall into the pit of more-than-physical speculation. We are not dealing with ultimates, at least not with ultimate ultimates. We may proceed. Soil, then, is the resultant mulch from the decomposition of rocks effected by the action of gravity, by the force of heat and light, by the play of air and water and ice, and then composed into a further complex by the rotten leavings of the very growths which rise therefrom. And further, these plants use their excreta (for plants do excrete) to break down the rocks below. The rocks above have been broken by weathering: the floor below is further quarried by roots. It is always so with nature — the strong things are weak, the weak strong. The mountains are brought low, we tread upon them, by motions in the airy waste; and then the excreting juice from roots has power to crack the stones beneath that soil and thus increase it. These are the mills of God that grind so slow but do grind exceeding sure. If we would understand the Order we must forget the clocks of men and attend to the time-sheets of nature. Soil-making is not a speedy process in our eyes: the rate is something like an inch of soil created every five hundred to a thousand years — or one-tenth of an inch in a century.

---

[1] *The Rape of the Earth.*

Loam soil is said to be composed of one-quarter water, one-quarter air, and one-tenth organic matter — 'it thus swims, breathes and is alive'. So say the authorities. Whatever the exact proportion of water in soils may be, we know that it is very great, and that in fact nothing in all nature is more important than water. The reader knows that. He also knows that this book is about trees, and he has been kind enough to accompany me thus far in the confidence that I will stick to my subject. That confidence is not misplaced. I learn what not to do, as well as what to do, from my masters. If John Ruskin had handled this theme, he would undoubtedly at this point have done a volume on Water. But I am all for sticking to one thing at a time. This is difficult of course, since *inter-relatedness* is the very definition of nature. The full theme of Water is a great subject and can lead us into many places and unveil some surprising spectacles; and perhaps if I get back to trees the reader will not refuse to join me at some future time in a consideration of water. But something must be said here and now about the hydrologic cycle since trees play an important part in the smooth working of its flow. Incidentally, it is also another pronounced example of what we are calling the Order of Nature. My best plan will be to make a general statement, eschewing all detail and all the fascinating by-paths of the subject. Then bearing it in mind, taking the water-wheel as given, we can return to our trees and examine the specific part they play in the universal scheme.

There is a given amount of water in the world, residing in ocean, air, and earth. The total is neither added to nor subtracted from: it is constant. Though constant in amount, it is in continual motion, passing in a ceaseless cycle from earth to ocean and ocean to air and air to earth. Its existence is necessary to all living things, and its *even flow* the prime factor in relation to their comfort and their quantity. Happily, over very large areas of the earth's surface the give and take is consistent and steady. The sun beats down upon the ocean, the ocean raises evaporation into the form of clouds which, like vessels, are shifted by the wind across the land. As the clouds pass over they are either obstructed or cooled and consequently fall to the ground in the form of rain. This is called precipitation. Having fallen, it may, if the land is bare, quickly evaporate again and rise back into the sky; or it may flow in torrents down a mountain-side into the valley below; or it may strike a forest and neither evaporate nor rush down the hill, but slowly infiltrate into the soil. It depends where it falls, but for the most part we may say that there is a satisfactory exchange between ocean, air, and earth so that the fall of water from the sky is neither wholly sent back to the sky nor quickly conducted to the sea again. It enters the earth, thereby supplying immediate life-giving elixir to plants and animals, and also conserving the land against days of drought in the form of lakes and reservoirs above and below the surface — for the amount of reservoirs and rivers and lakes below the surface of the land is nearly as great as above it, while the subterranean wells and springs are of the first importance in the economy of nature.

The hydrologic cycle therefore presents us with another aspect of the primal order; and if the exchange between precipitation, infiltration, and evaporation is evenly held, then the best conditions for living things are provided. Nevertheless my description above is incomplete even as a bare general statement. For there is a complication which makes a neat statement of the cycle, or the circle, impossible. In fact it makes the words cycle or circle a little dubious. I am thinking of the evaporation from vegetation. There is the evaporation from the ocean, and of rain sent up again from bare land under heat. That is one kind. There is another kind. There is the water sent up, invisibly sprayed into the sky by vegetation itself. A full-grown willow can transpire up to five thousand gallons in a single summer day. How much then a forest? Clouds can be made that way over the land, without benefit of seas. These are tree-clouds, not ocean-clouds. There is a cycle all right, and a constant amount of water in perpetual circulation. But we must not forget this cloud-feeding by plants.

No more of this at the moment. We are not likely to forget it, for our task now is to go into the theme of the ministry of trees in the government of nature.

§ V THE INFLUENCE OF TREES UPON TEMPERATURE, RAINFALL, AND SWAMPS

WE have seen how vulnerable the soil is. It could so easily be tossed about by the elements, if unprotected. Happily it is protected, in the natural state, either by a carpet of grass whose network of deeply diving roots holds it down firmly, or by trees that on a tremendous scale stake it down, the tree-roots ramifying in all directions, so that only a hundred trees occupying an area of five miles will be actually supplying, in sum, three or four miles-worth of cordage for holding the soil together. Thus when trees were regarded by the uninstructed minds of superstitious men as the guardians of fertility there was some sense in it. When they become simply 'timber' in the eyes of unsuperstitious and instructed men who cut them down indiscriminately the consequences are so bad that modern science is busy restoring the idea that after all trees do guard the fertility of the soil.

Let us now plunge into the centre of our subject. On closer examination we find that trees perform many more offices in relation to the soil than that of merely pegging it down. By virtue of cooling the air and spraying the sky and multiplying the clouds they exert considerable influence upon the fall and distribution of rain; by virtue of sponging the earth around their feet they enormously influence the behaviour of floods, the discipline of rivers, the supply of springs, the health of fish, and (when man arrives), the welfare of navigation; and by virtue of their power to suck up moisture by the ton they dry the swamps and control the malarian mosquitoes. Forests are so much more than meets the eye. They are fountains. They are oceans. They are pipes. They are dams. Their work ramifies through the whole economy of nature.

The rays of the sun beat down upon a barren place. The naked earth becomes very hot and the temperature of the air very high. But if vegetation covers that ground the temperature will be altered. It will be considerably cooled. For the vegetation will evaporate water. It has been proved that, in terms of corn, for every pound of dry substance produced there is an evaporation of two hundred and thirty-five pounds of water; and in terms of turnips, for every pound of substance nine hundred and ten pounds of water is sent up. Under good cultivation an acre can produce seven tons of dry substance. On these terms we can calculate that a given acre will easily evaporate, during the vegetative period, about three thousand five hundred tons of water which will mount upwards to moisten and cool the regions of the sky.

If this is true of crops, how much more does it apply to forests. And further, we must remember that leaves do not become heated nearly as easily as rock or open soil, while the ground under the shade of trees can never be greatly warmed. The result is that forests exert a moderating influence on temperature. That great mountain, the Brahmaputra, has not many trees; but its middle part is covered by forest — and there the temperature is less than at the bare parts by twenty degrees! The largest forest area in the world is at the upper Amazon, six hundred and twenty miles from the Atlantic on one side, and cut off from the Pacific by high mountains. So far from seas, so near the Equator — will not the temperature be very high and very dry? Yet no, it is not greater than at the coast, and not as high as some temperatures in the middle latitudes. This remarkably moderate temperature is attributed to the enormous transpiration of water from plants in the tropics. The rainfall-down is about sixty inches a year. The rainfall-up (or evaporation) amounts to forty inches a year. Between the two lots the air is considerably cooled.

And in a perfectly ordinary way, the influence of trees upon temperature is obvious to every woodman. Not only in the way of cooling the air, but of warming it. Let us have William Cobbett on this from his treatise on Woodlands. Here he is — commas and all: 'A coppice is *always* warm. In the coldest days that we know, when hail and sleet cut your face, and when you are really pinched with the cold, go into a coppice, and you are warm. In the very hardest frosts, the *ground* is seldom frozen in, or near, the middle of a large and well-set coppice of six years' growth, or upwards. Even in that bleak and terribly cold country, New Brunswick, where the frost comes about the 7th of November, freezes the river St. John (a mile across) over in one night, so that men walk across in the morning; where, in the open fields, the frost goes four feet down into the solid ground; even in that country, if you, in the very coldest weather, when, in the open air, you dare not venture *ten yards* without protecting your hands and face with fur; even there and then, if you go half a mile into the woods, you are in a mild and pleasant climate. I have, scores of times, gone to the edge of woods, wrapped up in flannels and blankets and furs, and, when I got in, reduced my dress very nearly to an English one, and set to squirrel hunting, even with my gloves off.'

This capacity of trees to moderate the temperature, besides being so agreeable, is also a factor bearing upon the quantity and distribution of rainfall. Water comes down from the sky in the form of rain or snow or hail, and is further found as dew, hoar-frost, and other condensations of moisture which form on the surface of foliage, branches, and trunks. And before it comes down, as everyone knows, it is tanked in clouds, or as clouds. What induces the exchange? Cold obstruction. That is why mountains promote precipitation. But wooded mountains are still more effective in deflating the fleeting vapours. Denuded hills do not always induce rainfall, while tree-clothed hills do. Dr. Paul Schrieber, a noted meteorologist, after giving elaborate data for Saxony, reached the conclusion that in a district completely covered by forests the influence of the forest in increasing rainfall would be equal to elevating the region six hundred and fifty feet. We cannot easily raise mountains when we wish to increase the rainfall. It is therefore worth realizing that by judiciously planting trees we can lever-up a mountain about six hundred feet.

This cold obstruction induces greater condensation in the air-currents — and hence precipitation. But also, forests, whether on mountains or not, add to the weight of clouds by the evaporation we have been speaking of. And since they add to their weight they induce their downfall. The amount of water evaporated, that is, thrown off by forests into the air, is so enormous that they have been given the name of 'the oceans of the continent'.

These oceans go up into the air and then come down again. The subject is rather bewildering. It is not made easier by the authorities. There are always those who insist that the case is not proven, and that our knowledge concerning the relation between trees and rainfall is meagre and tentative, the hydrographic methods of measurement resting upon anything but exhaustive hydrometrical data. Over against them are those who give elaborate instances checked by experiments carried out through a series of years. My information is drawn chiefly from Mr. R. Zon's *Forests and Water*. At the end of his Report he includes a bibliography of other pamphlets and reports on the subject, amounting to 1010. I have not consulted them all yet. But I have a measure of confidence in Mr. Zon, and certainly subscribe myself the humble and obedient servant of him and the other devoted men who strive to bring light to this subject. True, the instrument of language on occasion tends to break down in his hands as when he fails to differentiate with sufficient clarity the words *consumption* and *absorption*, or *evaporation* and *transpiration*; and there are times when he appears to be speaking of Transpiration under the head of Precipitation.

For it should be clear that when we speak of trees increasing rainfall — on the ruling of the above data — we are not talking about precipitation so much as of transpiration; we are not talking of rainfall-down so much as rainfall-up; we are not saying that the rain falls from the sky and waters the trees, but that it rises from the trees and waters the sky. Mr. Zon makes some remarkable observations. He declares, drawing upon further authority, that seven-ninths of rain is supplied by land-evaporation, even over areas adjoining the ocean. He maintains that only seven per cent of all the water evaporated from the oceans enters into precipitation over land. 'It may be assumed therefore that the moisture which is carried by the winds into the interior of vast continents, thousands of miles from the ocean, is almost exclusively due to continental vapour, and not to evaporation from the ocean.' And again, he declares that 'seventy-eight per cent of all the precipitation that falls over the peripheral land area *is furnished by this area itself*'.

That is equivalent to saying — When we stand in an area of forest in the interior of a continent, receiving rain upon our heads, it is primarily proceeding from the ground beneath our feet. If you don't like this, note the following from another honoured authority, Mr. H. S. Person, in his Report, *Little Waters*, sponsored by Roosevelt: 'Depending upon regional climatic conditions, a given store of water which has been blown in over the land from the ocean in the form of clouds, may be "worked" three to five times as rainfall, because of alternations of evaporation and transpiration with precipitation, before it returns to the ocean as stream flow.'

That rather supports my bold image above. Five times the sky has emptied a shower of rain on my head, and five times it has been sent back again before making its way home by river. It also supports my earlier statement that there are tree-clouds as well as ocean-clouds. The trees are fountains that invisibly spray the heavens with their exhaust. See yonder cloud hanging above the wood. There is a strong wind blowing, but the cloud stays at the same spot. It does not move on. The wind has no effect upon it. It remains above those trees, hovering there like a hawk waiting for its prey. It should have gone miles away by now horsed upon that sightless wind. It stays there because it is being continuously fed by the trees. It is being torn to pieces and scattered by the wind, but at the same time it is being renewed by vapours from below. It is not the same cloud that remains there, but a continuously created one. In the midst of life it is in death, and even as it dies it lives.

It will be noticed that Mr. Person is stronger than Mr. Zon on the offices of the ocean. For my part I am convinced that there must be a continuous feeding from the ocean. There must be some feeding from the ocean, otherwise it is impossible to see how there could ever be any tree-clouds at all, how there could be anything but drought. I must not pass anything on to the reader which I cannot successfully pass through my own mind. Everyone who writes on these themes is deeply indebted to Mr. Paul Sears's *Deserts on the March*; yet he writes (approaching this particular aspect from the other end): 'Forests tend to occur where there is a greater annual fall of rain in inches than the air, on the average, will draw back in evaporation. Where the reverse is true grassland occurs, or if the evaporation is still more intense, scrub and desert.' It beats me how he can suppose that if more goes up than comes down there could possibly be any vegetation at all!

Others will doubtless clear up this misty point as to the ratio of water given absorbed and returned. In the meanwhile a broad fact is clear: namely, that forests by feeding clouds and perhaps making some more on their own, increase rainfall; and that they do this not only for their own locality but for other places since the wind will often carry the vessels a long way before unloading. Thus trees are great distributors of rainfall. Water is not evenly distributed throughout the world and is not always found where it would be most welcome, and trees thus play an important part in its distribution, for not only do they at given places add weight to clouds and bring down the messengers of moisture, but also that vast vapour given off by forests into the atmosphere is often carried great distances, so that trees of one country may be the cause of rainfall in another that needs it more.

We can say this. Supposing that tomorrow there were no vegetation over the face of the earth — then much less rain would fall over the continents; the clouds would frequently pass over without unloading. If on the next day trees covered the same space, then the rainfall would be enormous in comparison. Therefore if continentals (we are not thinking of islanders such as the British, at the moment) wish to be sure of their rainfall, they should be careful about their forests. They have not always been thus careful. The result is that in some places after reckless lumbering, men have looked up to see the clouds steadily passing them by day after day without discharging their moisture, like ships refusing to put into port. The primitives were nearer the truth when they paid special honour and made peculiar sacrifices to certain trees as the producers of rain.[1]

Finally, it is clear from the foregoing that if we are entitled to say — Put up some trees and you can pull down some clouds (always supposing the actuality were anything like as simple as that!) we are certainly not entitled to think that this will always add to the moisture of the soil on which they stand. On the contrary, they suck up moisture, as we have just seen. 'The more highly developed is the vegetal cover,' says Mr. Zon, 'the faster is moisture extracted from the soil and given off into the air. In this respect the forest is the greatest desiccator of the soil.' As a rule, therefore, the best places for encouraging forests are the hills and the mountains — to mention but one reason. And from this it also follows that trees could be used to suck up swamps and bogs. Swamps are agriculturally useless and often the breeding-places of malaria and swamp-fevers. In fact trees have already been planted for the purpose of draining swamps. It has been done with great success in Landes and Sologne. It would be delightful to see the half-useless peat-bogs of Ireland's Calary Common in County Wicklow transformed in this way.

The above considerations, then, entitle us to say that trees have a decided influence upon temperature; that by offering obstruction to clouds on high places they increase rainfall and in effect raise the height of mountains; that though forests promote a greater fall of rain than do open spaces, they themselves give back almost as much water as they receive, raising invisible oceans which moisten the pastures of the sky and favour a far-flung distribution of rain; and that this very fact enables them to soak up swamps and cleanse their malarian pollutions.

[1] See FRAZER, *The Golden Bough*: The Magic Art, vol. II, p. 46.

YET that is only some of it. Trees do more than
that in the economy of nature. They hold up the
mountains. They cushion the rain-storms. They discipline the rivers. They control the floods. They
maintain the springs. They break the winds. They
foster the birds.

All the barren mountains of the world are falling
down. They are too unyielding. They can be overcome and undermined by the soft and the flexible. The
wind beats upon them and they do not bend. The rain
lashes them and they do not absorb it. The rocks are
corroded by the insinuating force of the less substantial
elements; the fallen water, finding no entrance in earth,
rushes down as on a roof and wears away the flint; the
fingers of the wind press ceaselessly against the cracks
within the weakening stone. This wearing of the water
and the wind, this 'weathering', may be slow; but let no
man build a cottage in the valley on that account; for
though the gullies take time to carve and the under-
mining seems insensible — yet tomorrow, today perhaps,
a landslide may occur and a big slice of the mountain
seek the plain below.

However, most of the mountains are held together by
plants (and in some cases by ice). This plant-cover
consists of grass or trees or both. Even if the trees do
not go up the whole mountain and only stake it down
at the middle regions, it still means that a high avalanche
will be stayed from total descent by the arms of the trees.
'A mountain without forest is an absurdity,' says Dr.
Ehrenfried Pfeiffer, 'and it creates a serious illness of the

earth's surface.' For trees not only prop up the pile, they attract rain as we have seen. Permit me to quote Pfeiffer in support of what I have just said under that head. 'The mountains are the great water gatherers of the earth. On them the clouds discharge their burdens; in the temperate zones and regions of the monsoon, the rainfall increases with increasing altitude, up to a definite point. Curiously enough the altitude approximates to that of the timber line. The precipitation decreases in the region of the Alpine meadows. It is, therefore, more accurate to say that the hills, mountains and forest, combined, are the water gatherers. The clouds strike against the mountains, forests attract the clouds — so speaks the mountaineer and woodsman on the basis of simple daily observations.'[1] Tree-clothed mountains, then, are water gatherers: we have established that. But, again, that is not all of it. They do more than gather the rain. They do more than hold up the mountains. They deal with the rain in the best possible way in the interests of natural economy.

Imagine if you can — it is not something we could ever see in the state of nature — a long mountain slope consisting of soil without grass or trees on top. When the rain-storm beats down upon it, what happens? Some of the water sinks in and is sponged up; and a great deal more runs down into the valley below to form a torrent making for the lowlands and the sea. The rain-storm continues: and now the water is hardly absorbed at all and ninety per cent of it runs down, *taking with it* a proportion of the top of the soil. The process continues. This very unnatural erosion continues and the rivers increase, while their freightage of soil and silt piles up in the regions far away. The process

[1] *The Earth's Face.*

goes on until all the top of that soil has been carried down. Then the bottom of it follows, the stones, the rubble follow and pile up on the soil which went first, so that matters are now upside down in the valley beyond. The storm subsides. The rivers decrease. The beds dry up. There is a period of drought. Then once again the storm breaks out. This time the water rushes down so unhindered and so swiftly, that what with inadequate river banks and gross siltage, floods sweep over the land.

This never happens, of course, in the Natural Order. It could happen if someone came and rolled up the carpet of grass and pulled out the cover of trees.

Now let us imagine the same area of mountain slope covered with forest. Again the storm breaks out and the rain pours down. This time it does not reach the ground all at once. It must first fall upon the leaves and the branches of the trees, and thence trickle to the bottom where it is easily absorbed. There is no running straight down the hill into the valley. For not only is there so much less force in the rainfall by virtue of the living-leaf obstruction which cushions the blow, but the dead-leaf and twig obstruction, the litter, serves in the nature of a colossal sponge, a single acre of which can sometimes harbour forty-six tons of water. This absorption on the floor is the chief thing and a very great thing: but the check first received at the roof is also important. This is particularly evident in the case of snow, the rapid melting of which is so often a cause of sudden flood where there are no trees. In a dense forest only half the snow-fall reaches the ground. A white roof is formed on top of the trees, so that airmen passing across forest lands have sometimes confused the foliage with the floor. When the false upper floor melts it must first trickle down the barks or fall in lumps to the ground. This capacity of litter to detain moisture is called seepage, which in many places on the steepest slopes has been found so marvellously absorbative that it 'creates conditions with regard to surface run-off such *as obtain in a level country*.[1] It can turn almost a perpendicular into a flat in terms of gravitation.

It is this seepage which promotes the discipline of rivers, the always wonderful sight of water running on and on all the year round, neither flowing over its banks nor drying up nor becoming clogged with silt. It is seepage which makes severe floods extremely rare in the natural state. It is seepage which preserves the water clean and wholesome for the fishes. It is seepage which keeps the rivers dependable for navigation when men arrive on the scene. Indeed it is already a well-known truth that if we strike at our trees and thus at seepage, we strike at our inland ships: thus (to anticipate the Argument for a minute), at the period of Roman rule in France the river Durance was perfectly navigable, while now, the watersheds being cleared of forests, you can hardly float a skiff on it; and the Loire, once a navigable river of the highest order affording communication between Nantes and the Central Provinces, so that in 1551 the Marquis of Northumberland, Ambassador from England, could sail from Orleans to Nantes panoplied in a magnificent suite 'in five large many-coloured boats', is now unnavigable above Saumer, owing to the detritus brought down from the mountains with every flood.

Moreover, this seepage provides such a system of sieving, such a network of small tributaries, such a check on too swift surface evaporation, that it not only

[1] PAUL SEARS, *Deserts on the March.*

regularizes the rivers but creates and maintains the springs. There is a world we know little about, we dwellers on the upper earth; a world open only to the eye of the spelaeologists, those daring travellers into the nether regions in which are discovered underground rivers and lakes and wells in the silent majesty of mighty halls and the total darkness of long winding corridors and caves. Here is the beginning of rivers. Here is the fountain-head of the flow, the primal source of the glittering glory we behold far away in the valleys and the plains. And it is *maintained*. It is fed slowly and continuously from the great sponges that cling to the mountains. This is the protection against drought no less than the only true damming against flood.

The consolidation of mountains and the just administration of water do not exhaust the offices of trees in relation to the earth. There is an invisible agent we have to reckon with; necessary and beneficial in the motions of the sphere, but at times a most blasting bane, an unseen foe that needs no cloak of darkness. We must consider the wind on the plain. It is not so drastic an element as water, but it can be a fearful one. Its invisible whips can be the scourge of man and beast and plant. The only thing to do is to break it. An impossible task, we might think. It is easy to break hard things, by simply tapping them or by elaborately blasting them to bits. It is very difficult to break a really soft thing; and when that thing is the unseen element of wind whose arm is yet strong enough to raise up liquid mountains on the sea or cast down houses on the land, the only thing we can do is to wall ourselves away from it. We cannot wall up the open country, so we must try and break that fury. Again we call trees to our rescue, and speak of Wind-breaks. And it is astonishing to how great an extent they do break it. I have stood on a field protected by a line of poplars when almost a hurricane was blowing across the country, and I have felt hardly enough wind to blow my hat off; while the difference in the temperature between my side and the far side of the trees was remarkable —no wonder, since it is found that even a hedge of only six feet high can raise the average soil temperature three or four degrees to a distance of four hundred and fifty feet.

We take this sort of thing for granted in the British Isles where agriculture is not yet so much the enemy of silviculture that hedges at least are still in abundance. One writes 'not yet' because hedging is a big job in itself, as I can vouch for from personal experience of it, and does not lend itself to any mechanical instrument. But since so many hands have recently been turned into steel, so many men exchanged for machines of one sort or another, the man who looks after hedges may soon be no longer found on a farm; and thus the farmer is increasingly showing a tendency to do without hedges and to put up one long piece of wire instead, charged with electricity for the benefit of the amazed and affrighted cows. I suppose there will have to be a decade of bovine electrical education before these monstrosities are exchanged again in favour of hedges. But elsewhere in the world, on great stretches of plain, neither trees nor hedges are naturally abundant, and 'the wind which sweeps over the plain unhindered, increasing in fury and breadth, is its greatest enemy. In drying out the plain, it creates a hard soil crust. By increasing evaporation, it draws off the soil moisture and cools the soil. Then it tatters and dries the finer soil parts. A plain constantly exposed to wind pressure will be driven back to the most primitive conditions of life and growth'.[1] And should there ever come a time when large areas of level forest are cut and the land ploughed and the soil loosened, then, the hitherto harmless wind in that region will be no longer harmless, and ruined farmers will face that cloud of dust which is their day of judgment.

Thus it is easy to see that the breaking of the wind is nearly as important an office of trees as the distribution of the rain, the ruling of the rivers, and the maintaining of the springs.

One other thing — the birds. We must not forget the birds. They compose one of the forces that serve the rhythms of nature. Their residence is in the trees. Can we dispense with their services? Without them can we keep down the insects in a natural way? Of course we are always doing it in our own way. We feel bound to do it in the interests of agriculture, especially fruit-culture. If we are to get the benefit of the earth — which belongs to us, we say — we must exterminate a great many creatures who are inclined to eat our stuff. Insects are the worst offenders. Their offence is rank. They must go. Many of them have gone accordingly. The trouble is that either they return by other entrances and perhaps in other forms, or their exit is the cause of increased strength in other quarters. The subject is wonderfully complicated. Probably every single thing in nature works for the ultimate good of the whole motion of life: if anything, however minute, were an alien performing wrong action, then, either it or the whole universe would surely come to grief. It might be

[1] EHRENFRIED PFEIFFER, *The Earth's Face.*

better to keep our trees and let the birds do the job. There are good birds and bad birds from the point of view of agriculture; but is it wise therefore to try and dispense with all of them? The sparrow may be our enemy on the field; but may we on that account dispose of the tom-tit who consumes eighty pounds of agriculturally injurious caterpillars in a summer, or of the cuckoo who eats eight hundred a day? The wood-pigeon may be our curse; but can we dispense with that excellent rodent-eater the owl, or with the starling who is the destroyer of the lepidopterous larvae? These are big questions when we come to weigh them in terms of long policy.

And can we take away the residence of the jay? His specialized knowledge in the best treatment for planting oaks, still amazes the experienced forester. With regard to his secret, Professor Bier has some interesting things to say. When considering the question of how many trees can be left to plant and spread themselves, he reminds us that acorns and beech nuts remain lying under the crowns of their respective parents. And since they do not grow well in the shade of their own species, the forester must operate artificially. 'In untouched Nature', he continues, 'these trees would have but a limited dissemination were it not for a very ingenious bird who steps in and cares for their spread in a wonderful fashion. This bird is the jay. He carries away the acorns and beech nuts, one in his beak, the rest in his crop, and sticks them into the soil, or far more often into the covering over it, especially into pine needle carpets. And he seems to do this in a much better way even than the forester. He re-forests evenly over the whole area, never puts several acorns together, but always at correct planting distances, so that a correct and useful stand of trees results.[1] Here and there he also sows in rows, again keeping the correct planting distances . . . I wonder ever and again over the fact that the wild pigs let the jay-planted acorns alone while they root up those planted by me, to the very last one, if I do not protect them with fences.' And a little further on he introduces a touch of metaphysics into these deliberations. 'In going about the building up of woods according to plan, no creature, outside mankind, approaches the jay; indeed I should like to say that he even surpasses the human forester. And this fact, apparently standing quite alone in all nature, which yet lies in plain sight for every observer, or ought to be in plain sight, is either not grasped in its implications and significance, or is completely overlooked by the experts, even though it is equally important from a practical as from a theoretical point of view. For whoever looks more deeply at once perceives the Logos. When I said that the example of the jay stands alone in nature, I quite consciously used the word "apparently". In reality something analogous happens frequently in nature. But again these connections are neither recognized nor attended to by mankind.'

For myself, I would prefer to use neither the word 'apparently' nor the word 'frequently'. We should accept these connections as the norm in the Order of Nature.

---

[1] In *Down to Earth*, I quote a German correspondent writing about the same bird in the same connection, under the name of the Eichelhäher — i.e. acorn-carrier.

# CHAPTER II

# MAN AND THE ORDER OF NATURE— THE OLD WORLD

## §I MAN REJECTS THE ORDER

THAT we might concentrate our attention upon a few aspects of the Natural Order, followed by a special reference to the activity of trees within that government, as little reference as possible has been made to man, save at the end about wind and birds. It was necessary that we should first contemplate the spectacle of nature exclusive of men and their activities. What shall we say of that primal state? how shall we value it? It is no garden: yet it is the only Garden of Eden there has ever been. It is no earthly paradise: yet Paradise is there. The earth-refusing idealism of man is at fault, not the creation. 'It is here as in Paradise', said the old Indian to Alexander Von Humboldt as they went up the Orinoco in a canoe for 1450 miles and frequently watched the many different wild animals coming down to the edge of the river to drink. But Humboldt commented: 'The gentle peace of the primitive golden age does not reign in the paradise of these American animals, they stand apart, watch, and avoid each other.' No doubt: but it is that or nothing. And the solid fact that few of us would choose the void as an alternative to this wonderful world, should be sufficient to prevent us arraigning the justice of what *is*. For here at least we can see that all things work together for good to this extent: that a balance of powers is held in such delicate and amazing equilibrium that water, air, and fire; that plant, animal, and soil live together as if they made a single organ: a balance of performance so policed that no unit ever gets out of hand for long. We are at liberty to call it hell rather than an earthly heaven if we wish; but we should pay careful attention to its composition before we decide to alter it.

This brings us to man. For that is exactly what he decided to do — alter it. He would *not* put up with all that danger, all that discomfort, all that pain and sudden death. He would not be eaten — however much he might eat others. He would not obey the laws of this jungle of nature, but get outside them. Nature and its primal order was not good enough for him, so he left the Garden of Eden.

He stepped outside. Let us change the pronoun — we stepped outside and became aliens on the organic body of the landscape. What happened from that hour to this is called history. But by history we do not mean the story of man in relation to the earth; by history we do not mean the story of man in relation to the other creatures of the world — that is not supposed to be important. Indeed, we have behaved exactly as if we owned the place; and while carrying out plans for the best use of the property we have provided ourselves with suitable religious and philosophic support by declaring that we happen to be made in the very image of God, and that the proper study of mankind is man. How we have turned to account the whole surface of the earth for our benefit; how we have gone beneath its surface and taken out zinc and copper and steel and gold and iron and coal, transforming them into towns and houses and machines; how we have used any animal that could be employed for our satisfaction and made a mockery of others for our amusement — is called the growth of civilization.

In many ways it has been a splendid story. Many of the forms into which we have cast our effort have been almost sublime. We can never wish that we had not used the peculiar gifts bestowed upon us by nature and had declined to take up the burden of our destiny. Since we rose up out of the earth and were given those powers by the earth, we can hardly be expected to feel overwhelmingly shamed by the irresponsibility of our actions seeing that we were made that way. Yet it is our saving grace that we are capable of self-criticism and even ready to declare that we should be responsible. And when self-interest comes into it we are even capable of mending our ways. We have reached a point now when we must revise our conception of man's place in nature, or suffer consequences such as had never occurred to us in the process of our conquests. In fact it is not unlikely that in the course of the next few decades — perhaps after we have had some really rude shocks — we will gradually return (this time on the plane of consciousness) into the Order of Nature, as one factor of the whole. If this happens, the turning-point will undoubtedly have been this century.

## §11 AGRICULTURE THE FIRST ENEMY OF TREES

'A LANDSCAPE', says Ehrenfried Pfeiffer, 'is an organism, a living entity, possessing organs and functions which react and interact according to definite constant laws.' Its arteries are rivers and streams, its skin mountains and forests and sea. This is a little far-fetched, perhaps; but nearer the truth than the idea of a landscape as a conglomeration of solids and liquids only connected in a haphazard way. In the above section I spoke of man as an alien or unassimilated body upon the landscape of the world. Of course, to say that he left the Garden of Eden to become an alien at once from then on, is not only very allegorical but it is to telescope the history of mankind too severely. He did not begin as an alien body. In fact he began, as we have seen, in so reverencing natural phenomena that he saw deities at every turn, and behaved, especially in relation to trees, almost as if he had scientific knowledge concerning their effect upon water and soil. Nevertheless, the step towards extricating himself from the bondage of natural law had been taken on the first day that he stooped down and picked up a stone with the intention of using it as a *tool*.

Largely, it was all right so long as man remained a hunter. For then his actions with regard to the earth and soil did not differ materially from the actions of the animals. But after about two hundred centuries of hunting pure and simple, much of it on open steppes, a milder climate and greater vegetation are thought to have stimulated the hunters towards a new idea. I do not know whether it is known exactly where or under what conditions a piece of earth was first *cultivated*. There must have been such a day — the most important in the history of all life on the planet. Now we have so much artifice around us that we tend to forget how artificial agriculture is. A field of wheat is almost as artificial a thing as a piece of pottery: it is organic, of course, but its existence in that form is entirely due to man and would be impossible in the natural state. To make nature grow things which could then be eaten, thus overcoming the necessity to kill some dangerous

animal or starve, must indeed have been an intoxicating
discovery. We still see much sense in it. There is no
more common sight than a field. And no one, up till
now, has ever dreamed of questioning the right or ad-
visability of cultivating a field. Since we owned the
earth, we could naturally dig in a spade wherever we
wished; that was taken for granted — and it was supposed that a spade could be used anywhere, a plough
driven anywhere, with good results for man. 'The cut
worm forgives the plough', said Blake, meaning that
nature is on the side of the agriculturalists. But is she?
It is very doubtful whether the cut worm forgives the
plough on all occasions.

There is no reason to suppose that nature is not just
as much on the side of trees as of agriculture, and we
are not entitled to suppose that the cut worm was particularly gratified when agriculture soon proved to be
the enemy not only of all animals who got in the way or
who could not be employed, but of the forests. The truth
is that trees were the enemies of men in the beginning.
Early man was obliged to conquer forests or be conquered by them. When he gave up hunting on the
steppes he was trapped in them. 'He could make no
headway', says Mr. F. Kingdon-Ward. 'He possessed
neither the tools for making clearings nor the knowledge
for raising crops. All the advantages which the tropics
conferred on him by reason of their wealth of vegetation
and easy climate were wasted. He could be a hunter
and nothing more. It was not until very much later,
when man *was* already civilized, that he learnt to subdue
the tropical vegetation. One has only to compare the
culture of the North American Indians with that of the
tribes inhabiting the Amazon basin to see what this
implies . . . For the jungle conquered primitive man.

Centuries were to pass before man conquered the jungle — if he *has* yet conquered it.'[1]

It was not impossible for man to be assimilated organically into the landscape so long as the population was low. It was extremely low in the hunting days. A family then required and received a living-space of fifty square miles. Owing to cultivation the Nile valley was eventually made to support one thousand persons to the square mile; and the Chinese sometimes managed to bring the figure up to seven thousand. Ah, it is a dread subject, this of population! I confess that when I think of it I am in danger of stylistic inelegance. It seems to vitiate all one's hopes — nay, all the good works of good men, especially of agriculturalists. It promotes such dreadful nonsense and such dreadful cant. The exhortation to 'increase and multiply' was pronounced to a race consisting of eight persons — not to the Chinese, or the Russians, or the Indians, or the Americans, or the British. Our approach is so insolently illegitimate. We talk as if we had a right to have huge populations — whether in terms of a nation or of mankind generally. We have no more right to do this than any other species. Not that nature cares. Whenever any species oversteps the mark in numbers or behaviour, it pays the penalty and meets with catastrophe. We consider this quite in order and recognize it to be excellent when some huge natural slaughter by starvation or cold overcomes some obnoxious tribe of insects. We approve the scheme. In 1770 the vastly over-populated continent of India was the victim of a famine in which ten million people died. That was excellent — as seen from the viewpoint of the animals. It was secretly thought to be excellent by other nations. Our turn may come tomorrow — and

[1] F. KINGDON-WARD, *About This Earth.*

it will be seen as excellent by others. Nature keeps this book balanced all right, since she has all eternity to work in. But our approach is so extraordinary. We really do seem to think that human beings should be exempt from natural laws. We even speak of 'the sanctity of human life.' We never dream of extending this amiable ideal towards our fellow creatures — and in any case the cant phrase is cast aside the moment we start a war (though modern wars have been much more destructive of property than of persons). We are perfectly ready, by means of our colossal numbers, to despoil the whole earth and use or mock or kill every other living thing thereon, while not expecting that as a consequence we should suffer at all.

It is many years ago since Havelock Ellis wrote: 'There are people among us, and not a few, who view with complacency the vast increase of the world's population everywhere taking place, people who would even urge the human procreative impulse to still wilder excesses. Until every square yard of the earth is intensively cultivated by Man, until the virulent air is soaked with the noxious fumes of human machinery, until the sea is poisonous with human effluvia, until all earth's shores are piled high with the sordid refuse of human maleficence, it seems to these people that the world will never be happy.' The voices of such people are not so often heard today, though in England (whose vitality is severely sapped by over-population) there are always those who advocate still more births in the name of Power. We must have more people of killable age to fight for us in case of attack, they say. I see the point. But it is like saying — Let us destroy England in order to save her.

Apart from this provincialism, the danger and the

horror of an over-populated world are beginning to be realized. But does this realization make the slightest difference to the rate of increase? Sir John Boyd Orr has just declared (1948) that by 1951 there will be 300 million extra people to be fed. If that will be so by 1951, how about 1961? Supposing we put our entire agricultural and silvicultural situation on to a perfect ecological basis, and produced far more of everything than we do now — just supposing — what good would it do if the crop of human beings increases at the same time? It staggers me when I hear eminent agriculturalists like Sir John Russell and Mr. Ralph Wightman saying cheerfully in public that things are not so black since we can easily produce more. No doubt we can. But what good will that do if an expanding agriculture only means an expanding population? Then all their plans, all their work, all their knowledge go for nothing. That is why I say this is a dread subject — it vitiates our hopes and takes the vigour out of action . . . Still, let us not fall into despair over it. I admit that it sounds worse in the aggregate. If *each nation* faces its own population problem, fearlessly and uncantingly, it can solve it on a sound ecological basis; and if any nation is lunatic enough not to do this, that is its own funeral — and it will certainly have funerals.

To return. In early days things worked out all right, even after hunting had given way to agriculture, so long as men remained ignorant and superstitious. They were humble and afraid of offending the deities resident on earth. They were free from Freedom from Fear, which means liberty to exploit or destroy anything you do not reverence — (and nowadays there is only one natural object reverenced by man). It meant that they were obedient to natural laws. Today this is called ignorance.

The thing is to use natural laws for our own ends. This is called 'ameliorative improvements'. This is where a little knowledge is a really dangerous thing. When man started by living in the setting of a simple huntsman he knew little or nothing of nature's laws, yet could not help conforming to them as did the plants and animals around him. 'Gradually, however,' says Mr. Paul Sears, 'and with many halting steps, man has learned enough about the immutable laws of cause and effect so that with tools, domestic animals and crops he can speed up the processes of nature tremendously along certain lines. The rich Nile valley can be made to support, not one but one thousand people per square mile, as it does today. Cultures develop, cities and commerce flourish, hunger and fear dwindle as progress and conquest of nature expand. Unhappily, nature is not so easily thwarted. The old problems of population pressure and tribal warfare appear in newer and more horrible guise, with whole nations trained for slaughter. And back of it all lies the fact that man has upset the balance under which wind and water were beneficial agents of construction, to release them as twin demons which carve the soil from beneath his feet, to hasten the decay and burial of his handiwork.'[1]

## § III THE REPLY OF THE TREES:
### THE BURIED CITIES IN THE DESERT

THERE has been no monumental study compiled, linking the history of mankind and his civilizations with the reactions of nature. No history of ecology, in fact. It is not until modern times that we have become aware that such history is the most important of all, and

[1] *Deserts on the March.*

perhaps the kind of history that we can learn from. But previous to the modern era we are rather in the dark concerning man's successes and failures to set up his rule within the government of nature. When today we are considering the future fall or stability of a civilization, our thoughts go straight to the respective soil situation. With regard to the past we cannot be dogmatic; but it is clear that long before machines arrived we fell foul of nature in many places on a large scale.

Nevertheless we should go carefully here. We must not suppose that every scar or waste place upon the earth's surface is due to erosion caused by human beings. That is going much too far. I fear that too many of our soil erosion prophets of woe — especially in England — are fond of making sweeping statements of this kind unsupported by the slenderest proof. There seems to be no limit to the rhetoric of their meditations. Gazing upon the watered waste of the Atlantic Ocean now flowing upon what once had been an arm of land, they are 'unable to resist the belief' — that is, they wish to believe — 'that the prime cause of the Atlantic disaster was deforestation and erosion'. Men who can think of trees only, cannot see the wood for the trees. They will stop at nothing. They remind me of the critics of Shakespeare in general and of *Hamlet* in particular: having adopted a standpoint they will say anything in support of it. Having claimed the sinking of the Atlantis for the deforesters, they then point to the grandness of the Grand Canyon of Colorado as further evidence of nature's reply to the transgressions of men. They flatter us, I think. We can hardly claim the Canyon as our doing — we must hand it to God. When we stand upon a floor in heaven, as it seems, and look over the edge down into those stony gulfs of earth, we know instinctively that nothing done or left undone by man has caused the abominable beauty of that rugged way. Anything set going by man must be thought of in terms of time, whereas here, if the agent is not earthquake, then we look upon a playground of eternity for the motions of the air and the wearing of the water.

Again, we must be careful when we speak about deserts. It is not true to say that all, or anything like all the deserts have been caused by man. There are some fifty-six million square miles of land, of which about twenty-two million square miles is desert or near-desert — that is, two-fifths. The root cause of deserts, of course, is drought; and drought depends upon rainfall; and rainfall depends upon the direction of air currents. If the right air currents do not pass over a given tract of land, then neither man nor tree can prevent drought. In such places neither reverence nor skill can avail those who attempt to live there: they are at the mercy of the merciless and withering scourge of drought. Man is not the cause of all the sealess seas of sand; he is not responsible for every field of desolation where neither man nor beast nor plant can find a footing. The full story of the deserts is unknown. Tablets of the tale can scarce be furnished by the yielding sand. No fossiled script can be unfolded. Here are no books of stone. And yet at any time the amazed adventurer may come upon a loose page scriptured by a lost city or a forest turned to marble. 'I stooped to waken a sleeping Bedouin and he turned into the trunk of a black tree', writes Monsieur Antoine de Saint-Exupéry whose aeroplane had crashed in the desert between Cairo and Alexandria. 'A tree-trunk? Here in the desert? I was amazed and bent over to lift a broken bough. It was solid marble. Straightening up, I saw more black marble. An antediluvian forest littered the ground with its broken tree-tops. How many thousand years ago, under what hurricane at the time of Genesis, had this cathedral of wood crumbled in this spot? Countless centuries had rolled these fragments of giant pillars at my feet, polished them like steel, petrified and vitrified them and imbued them with the colour of jet.'[1]

The history of this forest which once had bloomed in that now desolate place might well have to speak of its growth, its empire, and its blasting, long before the arrival of man. But it is true also that we can stumble upon petrified cities buried in the desert. It is a matter of cold fact as stated by geographers that 'the remains of ancient cultures, buried cities, and abandoned sites, going back at least five thousand years, have been found in most of the old world deserts'.[2] Consider the meaning of those words. They do mean, they do say that here! and here! — is now plain sand where once the waving grass was green: here! and here! — a lawn of dust with but a mast to mark the shipwreck of a city. We are impressed by the completeness of such shipwrecks when we think of the lost city of Cuicul in North Africa, whose temples and churches, forums and storage pavilions were only discovered by the sign of a solitary column standing erect three feet above the surrounding silt; or of the perished Thydrus in Tunisia which once held a coliseum to seat sixty thousand spectators; or of Thamugadi at Timgad, founded by Trajan in the first century, whose carved porticoes, public library, Roman baths, imperial theatre, and marble latrines lay lost under the waves of sand for one thousand two hundred years until a portion of an archway and the crown of three columns caught the eye of a traveller. What happened? We must beware of putting everything down to deforestation or crop over-

[1] *Wind, Sand and Stars.*    [2] F. KINGDON-WARD, *About This Earth.*

loading. In some cases the climate may have changed and the air currents failed in their offices so that the clouds passed by without unloading those drops which give sentence of life and lacking which the cities are as trash and trinkets — though some authorities declare that 'there are no real evidences of geologic desiccation of a region, namely from natural causes, within historic times'.[1] But at this distance of time we cannot pass judgment in all cases upon the cause of these conquests *by* nature.

Though we may not have created all the deserts, it is unquestionable that we have created some of them, and added to others. It is not certain whether the once fertile regions of portions of the Sahara were desiccated by the folly of man or the finger of nature; nor can we say for certain whether the once flowering section in the Gobi near Turfan, regarded as the cradle of civilizations, was turned into dust by man-made or natural erosion. We do know that four thousand years ago Iraq was the granary of the ancient world when the river Tigris enriched the empires of Babylon, Assyria, and Nineveh, as Ur, Khidabu, and Nippur were fed by the Euphrates; and we know that today 'the Tigris flows menacingly on a raised bed of eroded soil brought down from the hills when the plainsmen, seeking more water for their irrigation crops and more land to replace their exhausted soils, cut down the hill forests and were rewarded with uncontrollable floods that overwhelmed their fields and swept away their irrigation works'.[2] That land of Mesopotamia is said to have been one of the most productive in all history; it could support those Babylonian and Assyrian splendours which have become so fabled that

---

[1] FAIRFIELD OSBORN, *Our Plundered Planet*.
[2] JACKS and WHYTE, *The Rape of the Earth*.

they are veritable cities of imagination enthroned in the memory of mankind. But the time came when no captives could hang their harps upon the willows of Euphrates' stream and sit down and weep by the waters of Babylon — for there were no waters: the cities fell, and for the same reason as fell from glory and plenty the Holy Land, the land that flowed with milk and honey; and it was not until the great Allenby, of massive sympathies and searching intellect, stooped down to plant trees even in the middle of his campaign, that the fatal deforestation of Palestine began to receive attention and the waste lands to flower and shine again. We do know that before the fall of the Roman Empire a girdle of forest reached in Africa from the Congo to Khartoum — now changed by deforestation and resulting silt to an area of desert covering one thousand two hundred and fifty miles. We do know that soil exhaustion, crop failure, and land abandonment encouraged a steady encroachment of the desert on the fringes of the Persian Empire until sand and mud conquered the conquests of the mighty Darius. We do know that the same desolations of dust now rule in place of the weakened earth that had been so rich around Carthage in the days of Hannibal, and cover the very spot where, lifting the poison to his lips, the hounded leader said: 'Since they cannot wait for the death of one old man. . . .'

All this was early days. We shall see presently how in modern times, Man, so much more speedy in spoliation and skilful in ruin can lay waste the surface of the earth.

THE lost cities and lost civilizations of the world
have not always been found beneath the deserts.
Sometimes it seems as if the jungle had advanced or
returned upon them, and like an armed host, bid them
quit. Thus with 'the glory that was Maya'. In 1519
Hernan Cortez, the great Spanish conquistador, stormed
and took the city of Mexico-Tenochtitan. He did not
know then, and he never knew, that it was built upon
the ruins of the Mayan civilization. Five years later he
travelled across what is now the little republic of Honduras,
hacking his way foot by foot through an almost impene-
trable forest given over to reptiles and insects and the
odours of putrefaction. Had he turned aside from the
path he was cutting, by only a fraction, he would have
come to a little stream where he would have found in
the midst of all this luxuriant foliage the ruins of what
had once been a great city.

It was the city of Copan, the chief light amongst
others such as Tikal or Palenque of the Mayan civilization which existed between A.D. 176 and A.D. 620.
They are there still, far from all other human habita-
tions, lost in the powerful tropical forest which 'like some
sylvan boa-constrictor, has literally swallowed them up
and is now devouring them at its leisure, prising the fine-
hewn close-laid stones apart with its writhing roots and
tendrils'.[1] Copan had been seven miles long by two miles
wide, with streets and courts paved with stone, a system
of drainage and sewerage and with high central temples,
palaces and towers. Not only was the architecture
evidently most massive and imposing, but the sculptured

[1] A. J. TOYNBEE, *A Study of History*.

decorations pass through an obvious evolution from crude and angular carvings to a sculpture marked by purity of style and straightforwardness of presentation, winding up with a period of flamboyance. And the people who had built this city and others like it, had also devised a system of writing by means of hieroglyphs, and an intricate calendar based upon elaborate astronomical calculations.

These cities were built to last, they were not made to be abandoned. But they were abandoned. By the seventh century those streets were silent, those courts were still. The jungle returned. Nature took back her fields. Like beseiging soldiers the creepers climbed the walls. Groves grew upon the roofs of the pavilions. Wild vines trellised the rafters of the haunted halls. The massive pyramids sank into the greenery below. Not just one city but all. The glory that was Maya went down into the growing gloom.

Where did the people go? Evidently they trekked north into Yucatan, and established there an inglorious Second Empire until the coming of the Spaniards. And why did they go? They have not told us. Their descendants could not even read the hieroglyphs. This ignorance is to us an amazing thing. Nothing so much differentiates us from early ages than this matter of consciousness of what is happening and what has happened. Today anyone can know anything that is happening anywhere. Our sense of history, present and past, is like a great network of awareness drawn over us and knit by endless words. In former days a whole people could abandon their cities and move to another land without leaving any record of the cause — not even one tear-stained letter of a child who had lost her doll in the process. Nor any questions asked, answered, or

noted down by other races of the day who might have
been interested in so enormous a happening involving
what must have been great suffering and grief and shame.

And still we ask, why did they go?  It could not have
been due to pestilence — for they would have returned.
The solutions advanced today are all ecological — they
spoilt their environment and could not feed themselves.
It does not matter how well organized a society may be,
how massive its buildings or good its art, if there is not
enough to eat.  It is known that when they came they
possessed very sharp axes with which they were able to
cut down the forest.  It is known that having cut them
down they then burned them and planted crops in the
ashes.  So for some time there was abundance of maize,
cacao, beans, and other plants which did very well in
that splendidly fertilized soil.  But the organic material,
now open to excessive heat, evaporated much of its
vitality in gases and lost much in the soaking wash of the
heavy tropical rains.  Fresh clearings had to be made and
the old ones abandoned, so that step by step cultivation
advanced towards ever further fields.  Such is the modern
ecological solution.  'The Cities of the Mayas', says Paul
Sears, 'were doomed by the very system which gave them
birth.  Man's conquest of nature was an illusion, however brilliant.  Like China before the Manchu invaders,
or Russia in the face of Napoleon, the jungle seemed to
yield and recede before the Mayas, only to turn with
deadly, relentless deliberation and strangle them.'
Mr. Aldous Huxley takes much the same view in *Beyond
the Mexique Bay* when he writes: 'The clearing of the
forest led to erosion, and in course of time all the soil
was washed from the fields into the lakes.  The result was
doubly disastrous: the fields became barren and the lakes
turned into enormous mudholes.'

If we are to understand the calamity we must use our imagination and extend our sympathy. When they came they were faced with a formidable foe, as they saw it — the thick tropical forest. To have made any clearing at all would have been an achievement. They not only did so but built those cities; and we must see in our mind's eye, first the forest as it is again today, and then see it transformed into great buildings in the midst of populous towns surrounded by cultivated fields. What will and courage and force! It is not strange that it never occurred to them that the foes which they struck down would soon rise up again and advance upon them and drive them back. Yet so it was. The very methods which brought them victory and gave them increase led to their undoing. 'The transitoriness of human achievement and the vanity of human wishes', says Toynbee in this connection, 'are poignantly exposed by the return of the forest, engulfing first the fields and then the houses and finally the palaces and temples themselves.'[1]

Thus when Hernan Cortez passes along their way nine centuries later, he does not observe the great city of Copan hidden in the knotted mash of the foliage through which he is slowly hacking his path. Such drama can scarcely enter the theatre of our thoughts. It is too big. We turn away. We can stage Hamlet and weep for him — even for Hecuba. But not for the Mayas. Their play is too dramatic. We cannot really believe it. And yet we must. For we belong to a generation which having seen conquest of nature reach unexampled triumphs now looks round with alarm at the possibility that the pillaged earth may not be able to support us much longer. And in these days, accustomed as we are to so many bombed sites in cities, the idea of nature covering

[1] *A Study of History.*

up the works of man is easily appreciated. Nothing has seemed more striking to Londoners than the extent to which, in a matter of four years, the visiting plants have trellised with their living green the formless husks of ruin.

## §V THE REPLY OF THE TREES: FLOODS AND 'THE RIVER OF SORROW'

THIS idea that we shall have to mend our ways in dealing with the earth if we mean to remain on it ourselves is something new. We look back across the great civilizations of the past and find that even the greatest of them fell short in ecological understanding. This is true even of China. Of course, the peasantry of China has commanded the respect of all historians and all travellers. 'There is no other peasantry in the world which gives such an impression of absolute genuineness and of belonging so much to the soil', wrote Count Keyserling in his *Travel Diary of a Philosopher*. 'Here the whole of life and the whole of death takes place on the inherited ground. Man belongs to the soil, not the soil to man; it will never let its children go. However much they may increase in number, they remain upon it, wringing from Nature her scanty gifts by ever more assiduous labour; and when they are dead they return in child-like confidence to what is to them the real womb of their mother. And there they continue to live for ever-more.' And again: 'The land represents at the same time one great cemetery of immeasurable vastness. There is hardly a plot of ground which does not carry numerous grave mounds; again and again the plough must piously wind it way amongst the tombstones.' And once more, from the same passage higher up, he says: 'Every inch of soil is in cultivation, carefully manured, well and professionally tilled, right up to the highest tops of the hills, which, like the Pyramids of Egypt, slope down in artificial terraces.'

Much as I admire the Count, I cannot think that what he says here has in it as much soundness as sentiment. It is true that the Chinese maintained the fertility of their land for four thousand years. It is true that they manured with a careful eye to the law of return, their animals giving eight tons each a year, and every adult contributing excreta (night soil) to the measurement of an annual thousand pounds. Even so this is not everything. To live on this earth comfortably requires more good sense than they showed. Ecology is the art of living happily with nature. They did not display this art. Far from it. They produced so many *of themselves* that they were always compelled to live at starvation level. Their numbers varied of course, but the population sometimes reached six thousand to seven thousand per square mile! That is to say they sowed an extra crop: not of rice or sugar cane, of bananas or citrus fruits — but of human beings. They did not harvest this crop, and then sell it, or eat it. They allowed much of it to rot, and then ploughed it in. For periods of drought could not be faced by so many. Between 108 B.C. and A.D. 1911 there were one thousand eight hundred and twenty-eight famines, in the course of which several millions perished. In the famine of 1920-21 the death-roll was five hundred thousand, while twenty million were reduced to such hunger that they ate flower seeds, poplar buds, sawdust, thistles, leaf dust, elm bark, roots, and stones ground into an artificial flour as an aid to the digestion of withered leaves. This is scarcely the art of living.

Nor is this all. We cannot possibly say that they did well by nature. They did very ill by their trees. The deforestation of the Chinese uplands provides one of the worst examples of ecological stupidity. It is historically and geologically certain that what is now China proper was very heavily forested, and that nine-tenths of the Shansi mountainous area was tree-clothed. The trees were cut down. If there is one thing more famous than the marvellous Chinese agricultural terraces which did so much to control erosion, it is that erosion itself of the rich loess in the north which, when exhausted and loosened by removal of wind-breaks and root-grips, swiftly and massively eroded carving gigantic furrows on the face of that fertile earth until at last it came to look like a blasted battlefield 'scarred by forces far more destructive than any modern engines of war'.[1] It is not surprising to us — so wise after the event — that subsequent terrible droughts were interspersed by periods of uncontrollable floods. The loss caused by the undisciplined Hwai River, which in 1911 flooded an area larger than the size of Belgium, is said to be sufficient to have supplied food for ten million people. They have been obliged to hold in the rivers by means of earthen dikes; but on account of the colossal amount of silt brought down, these dikes have had to be continually raised so that now the bed of the river is above the land and liable to spill over — as witnessed by the floods in Chihli, Shantung, Honan, Kiangsu, Anhwi and Chekiang. As for the Yellow River or Hwang Ho whose very name means 'China's Sorrow', it is now as great a scourge as the Yellow Peril. It may be a glad colour, but it has a sad cause. It is China flowing away. Every year two and a half billion tons of China's soil is carried into the

[1] *The Rape of the Earth.*

sea by this service. This means twelve inches yearly taken away from an area covering one thousand two hundred square miles. Thus is nature avenged. Thus have the trees replied. An armed host of men came out against them and laid them low: and even as they fell, their perishing roots that had gripped the earth and checked the waters, were loosed, and the sins of the slayers were visited upon many generations of their children.

It is not to be denied that China built up a wonderful civilization upon the backs of the peasants. It is a big continent, and it was possible to go on for four thousand years before nature really showed her hand too severely. A mighty Wall could be built and a marvellous feeling of security prevail in the cities whose elaborate palaces with their Pavilions of Feminine Tranquillity or of Charity Made Manifest provided a suitable setting in which Empress Dowagers could wear capes decorated with three thousand five hundred pearls, and the Son of Heaven order a bowl of soup costing ten thousand pounds. The mandarins, the eunuchs, and the literati could subserve their masters and issue their elaborate memorials in a style worthy of a culture that should last for ever, while the pottery, the poetry, and the misty miracle of their pictures were perfectly congruous with the moral maxims of their sages. Master Kung might meet with opposition but not with indifference, and through the nobility of his demeanour and by the pearls of great price which he let fall from his lips as he wandered on his pilgrimage, he could establish an ideal of behaviour which seemed possible of fulfilment in so stable a civilization. The lofty exhortation of Gautama in the annunciation of the Law of Right Effort: 'Strive to avert the spreading of evil that hath arisen: strive

to avert the arising of evil that hath not arisen: strive to
aid the spreading of good that hath arisen: strive
to aid the arising of good that hath not arisen'
could fall into place in the framework of that day. No
civilization in the world has ever been more fitted to
respond to the quiet wisdom in the question and answer
of their great philosopher, Lao-tse: 'Who is there who can
make muddy water clear? If you *leave it alone* it will
become clear of itself.'

Today that framework has broken up, and we hear
only their cries of suffering. Are we to say that this is all
the fault of the West? We may have done much to under-
mine the Chinese with our wars and our science. But
must we not also say that it was impossible for them not
to break up if they over-loaded their soil? They have
rotted the foundations of their house — that is surely
unquestionable. The moment foundations begin to give
way, nothing can confidently be done in the house: the
gospel of the Mean becomes irrelevant, the pots fall to the
floor, the song dies on the lips of the singers, and Lao-tse's
maxim serves only as a reminder of the mud in the rivers
that are carrying away the soil.

It is right that in these perilous modern days when
the top of the earth is nearly everywhere showing signs
of exhaustion, we should turn an ecological eye upon
the fall of empires and the mystery of silenced cities
buried in the desert or lost in the jungle. Perhaps
we have had enough purely historical speculation. And
there has been enough denunciation on strictly moral
and religious grounds. The wickedness and luxury of
cities, the pride of rulers, the infidelity of an ungodly
and sinful people, have always made a favourite theme
for angry prophets and holy men. Saint Paul preached

in the City of Antioch against its pride and its sins. There were four hundred thousand people then in that city whose Pleasure Gardens of Daphne were the envy of the Mediterranean world. Today it is merely a drab little town in Syria whose former grandeur has been reconstructed after digging through eighteen feet of detritus caused by the silt in the Taurus and Lebanon Rivers carried down when the protective terraces had been neglected and the spoliation of the forests completed. 'There is after all', says Mr. Stuart Chase, 'no philosophical difference between the fate of Antioch in Syria and the possible fate of the Garden City of Kansas'.[1] No doubt Saint Paul was right to preach against the people of Antioch, and other prophets to lay their curse upon other cities. But they did the right thing for the wrong reasons. Those sins were not moral; they were not theological — they were ecological. That pride and that luxury might have been a great deal more pronounced and yet no harm befallen them; the green fields would have continued to yield them increase and the limpid water to bring refreshment: that immorality and that impiety might have spread further and mounted higher, and still the strong towers would not have shaken and the massive walls would not have crumbled: but because they had been unfaithful to the land upon which they lived and which God had given them; because they had sinned against the laws of earth, and despoiled the forests, and loosed the floods, they were not forgiven, and all their works were swallowed in the sand.

[1] STUART CHASE, *Rich Land, Poor Land*.

WHEN we turn to the imposing civilizations of
Greece and Rome we find that they had weakened
the foundations of their house in something of the same
way. Again, we must be on our guard against writing
history from only one point of view and saying: 'When
the mountains of Greece were cleared of their forest
wealth, their noble culture vanished, and when in turn
their colonists settled in the virgin forests of Italy, they
took with them the same destructive methods which in
turn caused the downfall of the Roman Empire.' Too
broad a generalization defeats itself. But the fact remains
that trees were venerated by the ancient Greeks, as I
have previously tried to show, and Mr. St. Barbe Baker,
from whom I have just quoted, is surely justified in
asserting that under their auspices 'the forests were protected by thousands of woodland deities and nymphs of
the holy groves, until the fanaticism of the early
Christians led to a war against these pagan strongholds,
in which the holy groves were destroyed by axe and fire'.
And what is the final result? The cool, definite facts
stand before us. After centuries of cutting and burning
and slashing at hillsides, the forests, which had once
covered sixty per cent of the land, now cover *five* per cent;[1]
and consequently every single region is severely eroded,
not two per cent of the whole country has maintained
its top-soil, no wild life is seen, and only one bird
sings — the raven.

Such is progress. We must look back two thousand years
before our eyes can rest upon their days of glory. It hurts
us now to conjure up that scene. We see a beautiful land

---

[1] FAIRFIELD OSBORN, *Our Plundered Planet*.

with a lavishly fertile soil, guarded by thickly forested hills and watered by never-failing streams easily supporting a *not over-populated* nation that had the security in which to erect magnificent buildings, to foster arts that should last for ever, to lead a full physical life, and explore with Socrates the paths that lead to virtue. Yet they were not wise enough. Man is laid upon the lap of earth. One main mistake — and slowly he goes down. The belief that there is nothing far-fetched in an ecological reading of the Greek decline is supported by the great historian, A. J. Toynbee who attributes the downfall of the Hellenic city-states to the exchange of the small subsistence farming of a free peasantry for large-scale cash-cropping with a slave labour force. Cash-cropping! — ominous phrase, and not confined to modern times. In the days of Solon, says Toynbee, this exchange was 'a tragedy whose gloom is barely relieved by a brief gleam of sunshine'. They had taken a false step. They could not retrieve it.

Elsewhere in his *History* Toynbee throws out some pregnant reflections concerning Rome. He suggests that the polarization of agrarian society into a handful of magnates and a multitude of serfs was 'one of the mental diseases of the Roman Empire'; that whatever spurious 'wealth' was attached to cash-cropping, it led to the depopulation of the countryside and the congregation of a pauper peasant proletariat in the towns; and that this revolution in their whole manner of life with nature 'gave the Roman people a shock from which they never recovered; a shock which revealed its dissolving and debilitating effects in the collapse of the Roman Republic, and in the economic decay of Roman Italy and ultimately in the decline and fall of the Roman Empire'. It was far more than a mere economic revolution. It was a naturally destructive process leading to a conception of the land as money and the forests as money. According to Mommsen, the 'free bread' given to the landless Romans led to the exhaustion of the North African farming, and that Rome would soon have starved had it not been for Egypt and the inexhaustible fertility in the regions of the Nile — which, be it noted, still functions, but is now threatened with disaster by the axes that are being laid to the forests far away in Kenya, Uganda, and Ethiopia! 'The decline of the Roman Empire', write Jacks and Whyte, 'is a story of deforestation, soil-exhaustion, and erosion. From Spain to Palestine there are no forests left on the Mediterranean littoral, the region is pronouncedly arid instead of having the mild humid character of forest-clad land, and its former bounteously rich top-soil is lying at the bottom of the sea. No people, however great and powerful in arms, could maintain its virility and dominance under the conditions that must have prevailed 1500 years ago in the Mediterranean, and no Dictator except Nature can restore the conditions that might allow another world power to arise there. That the Mediterranean countries have not suffered complete annihilation like the earlier empires bordering the deserts is due to the comparative rapidity with which new soil forms from the rock beneath. But soil formation has not kept pace with soil erosion.'

Such is the modern view. It is not one which would ever have been likely to enter the head of an eighteenth-century person. The age of Edward Gibbon was an age when Dr. Johnson said that it was far better to imagine a mountain at home than to go and look at one; when the Marquise de Courcelles made it a stipulation before marriage that her husband would never take her into the country; when Pepys expressed alarm at the sight of

Salisbury Plain; when a plunge in the sea was known only as a remedy for being bitten by a mad dog; and when Malebranche declared that 'the irregularities of the earth's surface, like the uncertainty of its seasons, are due to the fact that God has intended that our thoughts should be fixed on the world to come, and not on this world which is the abode of sinners — a world which He has ordained to be given over to disorder, as indicated by the irregularities of its rocks, and the cliffs of its coasts'. It is therefore in keeping that Gibbon, in the seventy-first chapter of his *Decline and Fall*, should blandly remark that 'the servitude of rivers is the noblest and most important victory which man has obtained over the licentiousness of nature'. Nevertheless, as the pen of the master moved towards the completion of his mighty work, he was constrained to observe how much Rome was exposed to frequent inundations through the increasingly undisciplined flow of the rivers descending from either side of the Apennine Range, until 'soon after the triumph of the first Punic war, the Tyber was increased by unusual rains; and the inundation surpassing all former measure of time and place, destroyed all the buildings that were situate below the hills of Rome. According to the variety of ground, the same mischief was produced by different means; and the edifices were either swept away by a sudden impulse, or dissolved and undermined by the long continuance of the flood'. He concludes by making the remarkable observation, with equal blandness, that the silt washed down by the river from the hills provided so great an accumulation that it elevated the plain of Rome 'fourteen or fifteen feet, perhaps, above the ancient level; and the modern city is less accessible to the attacks of the river'.

Today we are the less inclined to question such an assertion having witnessed results of silt which are even more remarkable, the most dramatic example being provided by Anatolia in Turkey where rivers, flowing from regions once wholly forested and now utterly denuded, wash so much soil into the sea that already some of the ports lie *ten miles* inland.

§ VII  THE REPLY OF THE TREES TO THE EMPIRE BUILDERS

CONTINUING our inquiry as to the success with which man has worked in with nature or failed to do so, we may glance at New Zealand and at the huge continental blocs of Australia, Africa, and India. We will find man in all those places. That should be a little surprising, perhaps. We do not expect to find monkeys everywhere, or horses, or white ants, or any other specimen. But the idea that we might not find man wherever we go is assumed to be rather shocking. 'Man is the measure of all things', we say. 'Without Man Nature is barren', said Blake. That at any rate has always been the view of the white man, his principle being that he should be everywhere, and that if any continent existed where he was not to be found, the discrepancy should be remedied at once. This used to be called 'colonial expansion'; and since we have invented words to conceal our motives, we can but applaud this amiable ideal. Thus with New Zealand and Australia. It seems that both those countries contained a small number of men who were sufficiently primitive to hold a balance with the rest of nature. When Mr. St. Barbe Baker recently took leave of an old Maori, he asked him if there was anything particular he would like to say. 'Yes, there is,' replied the old man. 'Fifty years ago when I was a boy, I rode with other boy friends on horseback to see a silly woman. She was not dangerous or anything like that; she was sitting on the ground by herself trying to catch invisible things from the air. She was the first silly woman we had ever seen. You come here with your brand of civilization, and last year your lunatic asylums in New Zealand opened their doors to 7500 fresh cases.'[1]

We have not only been good enough to set up these asylums as aids to our gift of culture; our silviculture is also interesting. We have felled fourteen million acres of forest and turned New Zealand into a 'great pastoral country' splendid for the grazing of sheep. It is splendid for sheep. But there is a difficulty here. It is not splendid for the land. Sheep are all right on the well-watered grass of an English golf links —cropping it nearly as close as a mowing-machine could do, so deep and thorough is their bite. Their effect on looser grass is devastating. 'Anyone who has not seen herds of sheep, each numbering several thousand animals, can form no conception of the damage to the land of which they are capable', says Mr. Fairfield Osborn. And the plant-cover that is not consumed is trampled and injured by the thousands of hoofs. This is now recognized by every expert. The final result of so great a deforestation followed by such grazing, must be and has been the old story of the natural equilibrium upset and the land eroded. It is only to be expected that men who are competent to judge are now declaring that the most urgent problem of New Zealand is the control of floods and the prevention of the excessive washing of soil down the short river courses to the sea, which is threatening 'to leave the country like an emaciated skeleton'.

[1] *I Planted Trees.*

That New Zealand grass, however, was turned into plenty of wool in the nineteenth century, and was good for Yorkshire. It gave warmth to a lot of people in England, and made others very rich. It also made the sheep-grazing farmers very rich. We may note in passing that one of the farmers who did extremely well out of desiccating the soil of New Zealand in this way was the celebrated Samuel Butler. Having put a good slice of the land into his pocket, he returned home with a large sum of money, and was enabled to spend the rest of his life in comfort at Clifford's Inn while he studied in the British Museum Reading Room, attacked Darwin, exploded the Victorian domestic interior, and wrote a fantasia in which he scratched at the surface of the problem of the machine. As a great admirer of some portions of his writings, it has always seemed to me strange that his five years experience as a sheep farmer should have had no effect upon him. Having returned home he drew an iron curtain down over that part of his life, and henceforth preserved a total silence concerning it. The truth is he hated sheep: (*The Way of All Flesh* breathes hatred of sheep). And he was ashamed of his farming. Not for the right reasons, though. He was ashamed of it, not because he had been a typical representative of the white man nosing his way into regions where he was uninvited. He was ashamed of it, not because he had filled his pockets by eroding the soil of a harmless and charming people. He was ashamed of it because the idea of having soiled his hands with soil was repugnant to his respectable middle-class outlook, from which, in spite of his gift for exposing humbug in others, he never escaped.

Some New Zealanders tell me that there is a terribly

ancient and alien atmosphere about the land — as if it did not want any human beings at all. Judging from some writers on Australia, the earth forces there extend little welcome to man. Indeed forty per cent of the country is a natural desert. After the natives had been disposed of, it required a great deal of courage to set up there. That portion which is known as the pastoral land of Australia where the 'lakes' only occasionally contain water and for the most part are salt-pans in which a spear can be stuck upright, where one hundred square miles is a small-holding and five thousand not the largest, where one sheep to every twenty-five miles is all that the land can carry without over-stocking, obviously demanded of the settlers more than the normal courage and endurance of pioneers. And with that kind of courage in face of powers so little friendly, goes reckless lumbering, a bare-faced fight against obstacles to farming, the sort of fighting in which the weapon against trees is not only the axe, but that method of felling by which tree falls upon tree so that they come down like nine-pins. When the weapon of fire is added to this the scene becomes such a bedlam of explosions and flames and splinters and shrieks from the trapped animals that it should be enough to move the heart of even a hardened tree hater. The very thought of ecology, of working in with nature, is laughable here. Australia possessed only five per cent of forests over the whole continent. They came down. One of the results may interest the reader of my earlier account of the influence of trees upon temperature: the low-lying lands on the coast of New South Wales are said to be now experiencing annual frosts, though hitherto immune; and experts maintain that this is due to the denudation of the forests on the surrounding hills.

There were the usual other results. The inhabitants of more fortunate countries can learn something of the miseries and splendours of Australian dust from Francis Ratcliffe's admirable study, *Flying Fox and Drifting Sand*. He describes how at one place during his travels the air became as thick as a London fog. 'Then all at once the sand began to move,' he says, 'and the ground seemed to be liquefied and to flow away in front of us like quicksilver.' He tells how holdings were abandoned one by one while drift-sand piled high to the windows, how stockyards were buried, and sand dunes became so elevated that the tops of the coolehah trees looked like small bushes. In bad storms hundreds of sheep are buried alive, while others, dragged down by the weight of their dust-laden fleeces, cannot rise and thus die of starvation. Mr. Ratcliffe speaks of visiting places where a dust storm was expected every three days, the people living in perpetual twilight behind closed doors and curtained windows, though even this did not prevent dust from covering their pillows and working into their bed-linen, while the only way they could be sure of getting dustless food into their mouths was by eating it from under the tablecloth.

Not longer ago than the end of the last century Kanga Creek in New South Wales was considered by Havelock Ellis to possess the most perfect climate he had known anywhere. A friend of his writing to me the other day from the Creek says: 'I have never known so much wind, and the less said about the weather the day I arrived the better. A gale blew up with torrents of rain and in the morning there was a queer yellow light and what I thought at first was thick fog. But I soon saw that it was not fog but dust. A couple of years ago I experienced a bad dust storm here — the one in which a lot of

Australia's good topsoil blew over to New Zealand. This one turned out to be the worst on record, and I saw in the paper that clouds of dust blew over to Lord Horne Island so thick that the departure of a plane for Sydney was delayed. That night we had a terrible gale and I was icy cold. I wonder what Havelock Ellis would think about the climate now!' To that letter I would like to add a few words from another received almost at the same time from another friend who had just driven from Sydney up about seven hundred and fifty miles to a mountain home in South Queensland: 'Some of the scenery is very grand with jagged ravages of mountains, but a lot of it is picturesque in a rather ghoulish sort of way — miles and miles of dead trees sticking up. They just "ring-bark" them and leave them to die.'

Strange and ghoulish enough! And more than extraordinary that a single tree should be destroyed in that arid lonely land where the melancholy traveller so often peers across bleak wastes to see twisting red columns of dust perform their macabre dance upon the viewless sands. These columns that are not pillars and support no palaces, make with their insubstantial trunks a wild warning against any destruction of the few trees upon those bitter shores. And perhaps it is not astonishing that even as I write I should learn from a report that last October (1948) ships sighted a thick wall of red dust over the Pacific Ocean, six hundred miles off the coast of Australia. It was estimated to be eight thousand feet high and four hundred miles wide — composed of the top of Australia's soil.

The enormous continent of Africa offered less opposition to plant, animal, or man. That various and rich vegetation could accommodate all who accommodated themselves to it. The primitive tribes inhabiting the country made little attempt to interfere with the natural order of things. Indeed they could not do so, and were obliged to fit themselves in with nature, and it is doubtful whether they even thought of the lion or the tiger as belonging to 'the lower animals'. It is clear that the inhabitants of the Ituri Forest did not suppose themselves to be superior to that aristocrat of the jungle, the Okapi, who with the legs of a zebra, the body of an antelope, the gait of a giraffe, with four stomachs and a prehistoric head, is justified in the pride with which it washes itself continuously by day and night lest one inch of its superb coat or white legs should be soiled. Fastidious, cold, courageous, aloof, a confirmed Solitary, an untiring wanderer whose home is where its bed may be and whose bed is anywhere, it commanded the veneration of *homo* still *sapiens*. It gave lessons in ecology: absolutely indistinguishable in the foliage, with eyes that can look in different directions simultaneously, with a skin that no thorn can puncture, with legs that are harder than wood, a head that is a battering-ram, and hooves that are cannon balls, it adapted itself with perfect assurance to its environment. The natives of the Ituri did well to honour such an example of perfection and pride in the equilibrium of nature; certainly they themselves, and others throughout the land, were no more aliens on the body of the landscape than the Okapi, and were in no position to abuse it.

This did not last. The time came when this huge country was to be 'opened up' for the benefit of races — from Europe. The complexity of motive, the variety of personnel, the comedy, the irony, the tragedy, and the farce of this business could scarcely be compassed even if one were in command of obedient words. Very superior men led the way, who, like Cecil Rhodes, by the magic of their personality, the canniness of their knowledge, and the intrepidity of their bearing, could not fail to force a passage; accompanied by manly spirits who finding their own civilization insufficient to satisfy their needs, sought fun and games abroad and called it Big Game hunting, leaving in their wake a trail of dead animals; supported by many pious men who if they found it impossible to make the inhabitants of the country they were invading worship their god, could at least persuade them to wear clothes; and followed by the herd of people who never have any idea what they are doing or why they are doing it — the respectable jackals and jackasses of the world, the mentally blind leading the blind, and the squinting the squinting.[1] When gold was discovered it became clear to all, of course, that it was our duty to take over the whole continent if we could, and remain there; and the story begins for Africa, as for so many other countries, of more and more aliens arriving on the body of the land, the flora being destroyed and the wild life exterminated, the trees falling, the rivers failing, and the soil eroding. There may well be justice in Mr. Vogt's remark, after detailed documentation, that 'the story of Africa, since its integration with the European world, is driven by an inner dynamic towards a fate almost as certain as that of a Greek tragedy. Upon an unfavourable environment with a low carrying capacity have been imposed progressive degeneration of vegetation, mounting losses of desperately needed water, and constantly aggravated soil erosion, which turn the spiral towards ever more unfavourable environment. Seen through the understanding of the ecologist, it is not

---

[1] Exceptions under each of these heads could not alter the Comi-tragedy.

difficult to understand why he has called the Black
Continent the *Dying Land*.[1]

It should be emphasized that it is not a question
merely of whether Europeans had any right to go to
Africa at all. Personally I am not interested in rights.
It seems to me far more sensible to use the word ideals.
We can have ideals and pursue them — that is, strive to
overcome human nature. But no person and no nation
can afford to moralize upon the naturalness of human
nature. There is nothing more natural than imperialism, whether in terms of occupying the field of the man
next door (if you can), or the continent next door.
Human nature has been like that from the start. There
is nothing more natural than imperialism: and also —
nothing more *insolent*. If there is a more insolent word
than *lebensraum* I would like to know it. 'We need room:
there are too many of us here: I think we will go there.'
'Do you really?' one feels inclined to reply. 'Is thats o?
But if they don't want you there, the proper thing would
be for you to be killed by them.' But the strange thing
is that quite a few of the *lebensraumers* honestly think this
quite improper and are morally pained at the idea. It
is best to leave morals out of it, either way. Start
moralizing and you must condemn what we all do all
the time on a big or a small scale, condemn human
nature for being what it is. Leaving rights and morals
out of it, the glaring and practical fact remains that such
'integration' is hopelessly unecological. Our methods of
farming for money may work all right for us to a certain
extent, but they do not work in Africa. What is suitable
in one climate is not often suitable elsewhere. 'Africa
illustrates perhaps more vividly than any other continent,' says Mr. Fairfield Osborn quietly, 'the ill effects

[1] *Road to Survival.*

of transplanting European cultures, and specifically European methods of using the land, to other regions of the earth, especially those lying in tropical and sub-tropical areas.'[1]

Once again trees give us the key to the situation. For on account of the abundance and concentrated intensity of the rainfall, destruction of the forest inescapably results in the destruction of its complex floor, the soil. And, when African forests have been destroyed, the temperature has risen as much as sixty degrees. Thus the evaporation is so great under the heat that when the sponging trees are taken away, hardly any of the rain can feed the water-tables, with the result that a lake such as Undur in Southern Libya is now dry during four months of the year, while in the single district of Mombera in Nyasaland, twenty rivers in the last forty years have been ruined as reliable watercourses. It is therefore not surprising to learn that the desert of Turkana, south of Lake Rudolph, is advancing at the rate of six miles a year. But when Europeans are out for profit in another country they do not take such things into consideration. The trees must come down — again by means of fire as well as axe. In the north-west of the Belgian Congo, five hundred thousand acres have been deforested, and in the western part fifty thousand cubic metres are cut every year without replanting. In Kenya only two per cent is reported to be left. The natives have assisted at these spoliations. Before the coming of the Europeans excessive lumbering was sometimes punished, as in Madagascar, by the decapitation of the axe-man on the stool of the tree he had felled — (shades of mythology!). We have taught them a more Christian approach and have pointed out that there is money in

[1] *Our Plundered Planet.*

trees, with the result that Madagascar is now one of the regions which has suffered most in deforestation, while Nyasaland which only sixty years ago was richly wooded and watered has now been totally denuded by native farmers.

Thus they follow our example. There is a way in which we might follow theirs. In Australia, since it was possible and more convenient to have the place to ourselves, we exterminated most of the natives — chiefly by means of arsenic, according to Colonel Walter Elliot. Some of the Africans are being kind enough to lead the way in exterminating themselves. Mr. Baker tells us in his *Green Glory* that the destruction of the forests north of the Gold Coast has promoted the rapid advance of the desert. 'Here may be witnessed', he writes, 'racial suicide on a bigger scale than the world has ever before seen. Knowing the end of the forest to be near, and with little chance of getting food, the chiefs have forbidden marriage, and the women refuse to bear children, for they will not raise sons and daughters for starvation.' Since the experts say that the threat of man-made deserts is a very real one to all parts of Africa, and not merely to those bordering on the Sahara itself, we must acknowledge that these people are setting an example in ecology which might well be imitated by other races.

Especially by the Indians. I am anxious not to exceed my brief. I am writing about trees and man, not making a total survey of our relations with nature. I am not going to say, and I refuse to be forced into the position by anybody as having said, that our treatment of trees is responsible for all our failures to live on this planet. Certainly not with regard to India. The root of their distress is so obviously over-population. They seek sympathy and food from other nations. It seems an unreasonable demand. They behave exactly like a man who should go into a field and say: 'Rather a poor field. Still, it might keep ten of us going all right, so that we could be happy together. However, let us ask a hundred more to share it.' This is done — and soon the dogs have the best time of it, since they are able to eat the dead bodies that lie about all over the place. A close parallel I fear — down to the dogs. Their attitude and practice is as silly as that — and no holier. We have heard much about the holiness of the East — from the East. One is tempted to make the clichéd reply that in order to be holy you must be whole. It is very difficult to be whole if you do not take *matter* seriously — which, after all, is just as great a mystery as *soul*.

It is not my intention to say a single word on the subject of India's agricultural problem. Her wealth of forests is still enormous. But again, great caution is called for in using them. I would like to conclude with one quotation in this connection from Mr. S. Jepson, former Bombay Correspondent for the *Daily Telegraph*. It is welcome to have observations such as this from a man-on-the-spot, as opposed to the vague disclaimers of those who always cry 'not proven' when the influence of trees on climate is brought up. He says: 'A good deal of land has been cleared in recent years because of the high price of timber, but it would be foolish to fell indiscriminately, because the problem of afforestation is closely linked with the major problem of soil erosion, and even with that of climate. Vast areas of India which have been wantonly cleared of forest have had their climate changed almost beyond recognition; rainfall has so diminished that even habitation has become difficult.'

# CHAPTER III

# MAN AND THE ORDER OF NATURE—
# THE NEW WORLD

## §1 EXTERMINATION OF THE INDIANS

THREE hundred years ago the whole of the North American continent was six thousand years behind European civilization. It was only inhabited by Red Indians, and not more than a million of them, while long stretches of wild meadow and primeval forest, extending like years into the distance, had no human dwellers at all. A wildly beautiful land, enormously fertile, carrying but a million Indians — it is difficult to conceive now. When we remember the Red Indians and the things they did not want, the clothes they did not wear, the houses they did not build, the roads they did not need, the laws they did not make, the goods they did not sell; when we consider how they could see in the dark, how they could run swifter than wild horses, how they could wrestle with the eagle on equal terms, how they could hear over immense distances, how they could run naked in the snow and frost without feeling cold; how they lived with nature from sunrise to sunset; when we consider these things and then think of the modern civilizations in general and of America in particular, does it not seem that machines have taught us to pursue one goal above all others — *comfort*? Part of natural life is discomfort. Can we really eliminate it?

In the compass of three hundred years that wonderful

continent was Europeanized — only rather more so — and plastered with towns and tied up with roads and machines, while the population increased by one hundred and forty-nine million. And now, today, after that three hundred years, we hear voices raised in extravagant prophecy, declaring that in *one hundred* years there will be no soil left on the top of the land, and that it will not support a single man.

But not so fast. Let us proceed quietly.

We have just passed in review some of man's failures to live within the balance of nature. Perhaps the most obvious example of a culture *not* working at her expense and therefore not suffering shocks, is that of the North American Indians. 'Nature needs to be let alone', writes Mr. Donald Culross Peattie, the American naturalist and gifted writer. 'Free to her own devices, she cleans her own house, knows no wastage, makes no biological mistakes. She solves for herself the problem which men are still finding insoluble — that of a balanced economy.' And the Red Indians let her alone. 'The red man never dammed a stream, never drained a swamp, never exterminated an animal. What ground he cleared for his primitive agriculture was negligible. On the prairies he lit fires sometimes to round up the game, but the only lasting result was to keep the Appalachian hardwood forest wall pushed back to the east, preventing it from encroaching upon the prairies, the great meadow, the American steppe-land on which the bison herds depended for their lives. In no way did the Indian break the charmed circle of the wildlife community.'

It is not my task here to appraise or dispraise their remarkable social life and religious sense which open up vistas not only of beauty but of horror and cruelty. Our concern is with the Indian attitude to nature. It was the polar opposite to those who came from Europe to destroy them. They fed themselves very largely by hunting — becoming quadrupeds themselves in pursuit of the bison, by dressing in wolves' clothing. Their agriculture was largely confined to maize, which, so far from being regarded merely as 'a crop' was the Great Mother. Just as the sun was not merely 'a ball of incandescent fire' but (for some of them) Uiracocha the Lord of Reproduction, so an ear of white maize, with its tip painted blue to represent the sky, and with four blue lines running down it, symbolized the dwelling place of the Spirits and the four paths by which they would descend to minister unto man in answer to the prayer uttered at the Procession of Peace: 'Mother Corn, Oh hear! . . .' And the soil was not less maternal than the maize. When Smohalla of Nevada received agricultural instructions from Washington he replied: 'You ask me to plough the ground. Shall I take a knife and tear my mother's bosom? Then when I die she will not take me to her bosom to rest. You ask me to dig for stones! Shall I dig under her skin for bones? Then when I die I cannot enter her body to be born again. You ask me to cut grass and make hay and sell it and be rich like white men. But how dare I cut my mother's hair?' Nor was the veneration of trees by the Indians any less pronounced. Believing that every natural object possessed its spirit, they attached special importance to the shades of trees and approached the cottonwoods as if they were beings of higher intelligence than themselves, and believed that misfortune would follow if due respect was not paid to them, while their respect for the acacia was so great that the offerings of blankets and ribbons and ponchos, and the gift of tattered garments drooping from the boughs often made it look like an old-clothes shop.

It was shortly after the above reply by Smohalla that the Hotchkiss guns of the invaders were trained upon the camp of the Sioux tribe, pouring two-pound explosive shells at the rate of fifty a minute, mowing down everything alive, until two hundred Indian men, women and children were lying dead or wounded on the ground while the remainder fled into a ravine to be pursued and massacred.

Mr. Harold Nicolson tells how when lecturing in America he was generally asked by someone in the hall after a lecture: 'What about India? How can you justify the British behaviour to the Indians?' At last exasperated one day, he turned and replied: 'Which Indians? Ours or yours? We educated ours. You massacred yours.' After a painful silence of astonishment at this rejoinder, Mr. Nicolson says, 'they had the decency to laugh'. An excellent exchange. And yet one cannot help feeling that the proceedings would have been rounded off more completely if someone from the body of the hall had then asked Mr. Nicolson: 'Who do you mean by you?' For it happens that there were no Americans in those days: only Europeans — and chiefly Anglo-Saxons who, stimulated by the initial example of the Pilgrim Fathers who first falling upon their knees, as the saying goes, then fell upon the Indians. We are about to consider the way of Americans with trees and soil; but we cannot say at what exact point we are entitled to dissociate ourselves from them and draw back the hem of our garments. But of course the Americans are proud of the early achievement in conquering the wilderness and do not wish to be excluded from that aspect. A good way out, adopted by Mr. Peattie, is to refer to 'our ancestors'. Thus he says: 'the task was to clear a space around the coastal settlements; to leave the Indians no lurking place; to push back the toppling green wave of the forest; to give the dreamer's mind room to think. Then the pioneers planted the seeds of civilization. Our ancestors, unlike the Spanish in the New World, did not bring civilization to the natives: we got rid of the natives and kept civilization for ourselves'.

When they had got rid of the natives it only remained to take over the property. A new, vast, uninhabited country lay open before them. Endless forests and long-drawn virgin vales such as had never before and would not again confront the eye of an invader, were theirs for the taking. 'They entered an Eden such as the world will never see again, the last unspoiled wilderness of the temperate zone, teeming and complete with a life of its own.' The empire of the trees occupied an area larger than any European country save Russia. Rooted in deep, rich, primeval loams, the beech forests of the Middle West produced enough nuts — a billion bushels it is said — to feed the passenger pigeons who flying a mile a minute hour after hour sometimes for days on end, clouded the sky by their prodigious numbers.

The Indians — few in any case — dwelling within the gigantic sweep of the plains had formed no concentrated settlements. They had possessed no machines. They had used no ploughs. They had kept no cattle. Food was for use and not for sale. Thus there had been no need to make demands upon the soil, and they had always preserved a sense of their dependence upon the natural environment. So when the whites achieved vacant possession they found one of the most bountifully endowed continents in the history of the world, in perfect condition. Nothing had been lost in the process of natural erosion — neither soil itself, nor minerals in the soil. The 820 million acres of forest held the continent in a grip which neither water nor wind could possibly disturb. The 600 million acres of grassland were no easier to shift. Nor was there any danger of losing the 430 million acres of open woodland. The desert-scape, which amounted to 50 million acres, was held at a minimum by the play of forces in the natural equilibrium. The rainfall, whether gentle or torrential, was forced to pass through a scheme of drainage which ensured that its distribution was expansive, its flow orderly, and its composition beautifully pure.

Perhaps the continent had remained like this for some twenty thousand years. Then in 1630, that famous Ship, described by Milton as built in the eclipse and rigged with curses dark, landed upon the shore. The passengers came with big ideas. They saw at once that this Order of Nature was not good enough. They must exchange it for one of their own — with their convenience as the criterion of its excellence. In three hundred years they achieved this.

## § II THE CAMPAIGN AGAINST THE FORESTS

HAVING conquered the Indians, they turned to nature. They found themselves confronted with a mighty host. It stood before them, erect and menacing, battalion behind battalion. But it was unarmed. It could not defend itself. It could not even retreat, for it was rooted to the ground. Being pious folk, the invaders saw that God was clearly not on the side of these green battalions. The forest was an enemy that could be destroyed. And they set to work to destroy it.

Two immediate objectives were to be gained: first, room in which to grow crops, and second, the supply of timber with which to build the new civilization and to maintain it with fuel. It was a big job, this subduing of the wilderness. It took toughness and time before the first 100 million acres of trees had been brought down. They went at it with a will. They launched a campaign against the forest with a virulence that seemed akin to hatred — (an attitude towards trees which seems to have remained with Americans to the present time, for in 1917, according to Dr. Pfeiffer, when some French peasants asked American soldiers to thin out a few trees, they were appalled by the recklessness and violence with which they set to work). They went out against the forests with the thoroughness of an invading army, attacking first one stronghold then another. For a hundred years the white pine trees of New England held out. Then one day it was found that all had fallen on that field. After the white then the yellow. The movement of destruction advanced relentlessly onwards from the forests of Maine to New York. In ten years those battalions were defeated and the lumber-troops entered Ohio and Indiana and Pennsylvania, from whence they moved in turn to Michigan, to Wisconsin, to Minnesota and thence again to the Gulf and Pacific coasts. That was the Northern campaign against the trees. There was a similar offensive in the South, through the Rocky Mountain region, through Arizona, Colorado, and Idaho, and from the Carolinas to Texas.

Such is the briefest possible outline of the onslaught. Today it is reported that seven-eighths of the continent's virgin forests has gone, and that only the douglas fir is making a last stand along a fifty-mile front between the top of the Cascade Mountains and the Pacific.

The method throughout this tree-war was that of clean cutting, complete clearing without any policy of further yields. It was applied to areas which had no farming possibilities with as much zest as on the fertile loams. Whole mountain ranges were burned off, though quite useless for farming. The attackers advanced upon the enemy with steel and fire — with quite as much fire as steel. Burning down forests by deliberate intent was one of the quickest means of advance, for in a wind fires sometimes spread at sixty miles an hour. Speaking of the Southerners, Paul Sears says: 'To the settler, here as in the North, the forest was a hostile thing, occupying the ground which he needed for corn and beans, even though it furnished him with game, fuel and building material. All was fair in the struggle against this handi-cap, and no weapon, not even his sharp ax, was more powerful than fire. So the use of fire against the forest became a ritual of the poor white. He has literally burned his way west, from the pine-lands of the Carolinas to the blackjack cross-timbers of Oklahoma and Texas.'

There seems to have been no sense of waste in those days. Often enough they did not stack the logs for later use — it was easier to get them out of the way by burning them at once. Thus it is told how, in the neighbourhood of Michigan, huge slabs of white pine were dumped into the open fields in great pyres and burned day and night — with such a blaze that there was no darkness in the town. Such pyres were sometimes kept burning for two or three years! Furthermore, accidental fires were ex-tremely common, and still are in America to the extent of one hundred and fifty thousand a year. When at last this became recognized as a menace and men were engaged at high wages to fight forest fires, it only made matters worse — the number of fires increased because out-of-work men started some more in order to be paid for putting them out.

It will be seen from the above that at first the lumber trade was of less account than the actual business of clearing the ground for cropping. But the steady growth of mill-power at length made the lumber merchant very rich and powerful. When we realize that the first water-power mill in 1631 could only cut 1000 board feet a day; that in 1767 the gang-saw cut 5000 a day; that in 1820 the circular saw cut 40,000 a day; that in 1830 the steam saw cut 125,000 a day; and that the figure is now 1,000,000, we can appreciate what the lumber industry began to mean, and with what ruthlessness the Lumber Kings would ravage their way through the trees with an even greater recklessness than the farmers. Forests once covered six-sevenths of the State of Wisconsin with hemlock and pine, and by 1899 the lumbermen, employing 1033 saws, were cutting 34 billion feet a year, until in 1932 there was nothing left. We may fairly call these lumber merchants tree-butchers since wood bore no more relation in their minds to the living object than slabs of meat are related to an animal in the eyes of the butcher. The trees were not trees but dollars in terms of 'timber' to be translated by the marvellous ingenuity of man into all the things, the endless things, required by civilization.

One of these things is paper. Perhaps it is when we turn from the saw mills to the paper mills of the factories in the towns that we get the clearest picture of such transformation. Let me bring the story up to date. At the time of writing this book — 1948 — the remarkable metamorphosis of trees into print is still in full swing and the facts concerning it are forthcoming from reliable sources of information. An average issue of the *New York Times* of ninety-two pages, plus book supplement and magazine pages, requires *one hundred acres* of forest for its production. Some American Sunday papers run to one hundred and twenty-eight pages and have a circulation of one million. This requires the pulp-wood production of *one hundred and forty* acres for each issue. Since this means the consumption, for each issue, of one thousand one hundred and twenty cords of pulp-wood, the operation demands the use of fifteen thousand, six hundred and eighty trees.

In my mind's eye, as I write these words, I can very clearly see what fourteen acres of trees mean. For it was once my job, as a woodman, to thin a wood of about that size.[1] It seemed quite a large area to me. That a space of one hundred and forty acres should be needed for a newspaper edition, is difficult to believe; and I did not believe it until I received an authoritative and very detailed communication on the subject from the Director of the Canadian Forestry Association — and the facts are as given above. So I must accept it as a fact that every Sunday when an American family open their weekly newspaper, they are entitled to say — Here goes another fifteen thousand trees.

We have come a long way from the conception of trees as gods.

§ III  THE CAMPAIGN AGAINST THE
PRAIRIES

THIS great campaign towards the annihilation of the American forests was a very big movement involving an army of several million deforesters in one capacity or another. A movement on the grand scale must always be informed with an Idea. It must have its philosophy. It must proclaim a doctrine. This was not

[1] See *Down to Earth*, part II.

lacking here. The philosophy of the invaders of this huge and bountiful continent was the philosophy of *inexhaustibility*. The idea was simple: there is no limit to the wealth in this country. The doctrine was pure: we are the masters and lords of this land, and may do as we please. The command was clear: pillage and pass on! — there is more beyond.

This philosophy seemed particularly applicable in relation to the soil itself. Here was richness. Here was fertility. Here in the forest clearings was loam which harboured the unpublished virtue of accumulated centuries, and had received into itself year after year the tribute of fallen leaves charged with the chemical elixirs of the air. It was natural that when they grew crops in such places, or in the ashes of forest fires, very good results were achieved. It was considered unnecessary to husband such resources. In many cases there was little thought of husbandry at all. For the first time in history fields began to be thought of as growth-factories. Step up production where such remarkable crops are possible. Repeat this again and yet again. Consider the plants as 'plants' in the industrial sense. Regard the idea of humus as humorous. Defy the laws of rotation and return. Take no notice of nature's rule of variety, and spread monocultures over large areas. The results will be good for some time at any rate, and if eventually the plant shows diminishing returns, why then we can move on to fresh pastures, for this is the land of Space, and we are the children of Speed — symbolized by our automobiles . . . And if they did not move forward in their cars, it would not matter to them; they would have cashed their crops and filled their pockets sufficiently to set up in the towns.

That was the general philosophy of agriculture. All

the settlers cannot have subscribed to it. We may be sure that some men must have thought that they would find a quiet haven in a new world where they could live at liberty and work with nature, and that having built up their own little homesteads with a few chance boughs and scattered stones, they could remain in peace for evermore. There must have been some such whose voices now are silent and whose homes are buried in the dust. But that was *not* the spirit of the time, the pioneering, pushing, gold-digging spirit. There were always astute men out to do big business in a big way, and it was they who set the conditions of life in this new world. And they had their sub-philosophy of agriculture — which was dig in a spade *anywhere*. That was the idea, dig it in anywhere — regardless of whether it is on the side of a hill or at the bottom of a tree-denuded valley. And plough at speed on a vast scale wherever the blades will go.

A green girdle of protection had been thrown over the whole continent by virtue of forests and grass. The forests were cut down. Then came the plough to knife its way through the prairies, and thus tear the skin off the land in enormous patches. I do not exaggerate. The American plough has been named the Destroyer. To anyone who loves the plough, as I do who have known no greater happiness than when I handled one, the American story here is painful. It is the attitude of these lumberjacks tearing down the trees, and of the so-called ploughmen tearing up the grass with tractors drawing batteries of ploughs, that seems to some of us in the Old World to be so abominable. The idea of feeling reverence towards the earth would have seemed to them immoral and even bordering upon the blasphemous. They were conquerors of nature — at speed.

They did not beat their swords into ploughshares; they used their ploughshares as swords with which they could rip up millions of acres into a loose soil exposed to the winds on the wide open spaces. . . .

'. . . Only a man harrowing clods In a slow silent walk With an old horse that stumbles and nods Half asleep as they stalk.' Their idea of a ploughman was very far away indeed from that man on the Dorset field in Thomas Hardy's poem. Their prototype was Tom Campbell, a Ploughing Magnate or King, who ploughed nine million acres and often used five thousand gallons of gasoline a day.

§ IV THE CAMPAIGN AGAINST THE
ANIMALS

THE great offensive of deforestation and ploughing-up of the prairies did not exhaust their campaign against the green girdle. They employed cattle and sheep to eat it and trample it. They introduced a colossal live-stock 'industry'. If unexampled profits were to be made from the trading of wheat and timber, why not from beef and wool? To this end they must first remove all other creatures who might get in the way. They must declare war upon the empire of the animals. 'In veracious recordings', says Mr. Peattie, 'we have glimpses of deer, elk, antelope and bear, raccoon and fox, water fowl and salmon, whose profusion at the time of the white man's coming made this virgin land the richest in wild-life he had known within the memory of his race. But when the white chips flew out of the first tree he assaulted, the ring of steel on living timber was the sound of doom for an immemorial order.' When the forest fires swept across thousands of acres, think what this meant in horror and suffering for countless children of the woods.

Let us pause to remember that there is nothing at all new in this extermination of wild animals by man. Europeans both today and previously have shown their prowess in this capacity. The land of Greece used to be celebrated for the abundance of its wild creatures. A recent traveller through all parts of the country is reported as stating that during all his journeys through the mountainous part of the land he saw but two pair of partridges and one rabbit; and as he travelled past the scarred and tree-wrecked hillsides, hoping that he might at least be able to watch the flight of birds, he was disappointed even in this and was obliged to be content with one visitant only, a bird in black (gone into mourning for the rest) that croaked by the wayside, a raven. Nor have we been backward in this respect in Africa. Apart from the broad policy of killing off any animals that offer themselves as fair game, it happens that the campaign against the famous Tsetse Fly which is the scourge of man and of employed animals, has caused the authorities to order the destruction of 300,000 wild animals who are thought to be the carriers of the pest — though, as Mr. Fairfield Osborn observes, if those particular animals do not serve as host, presumably other species will afford hospitality to the fly.

To take one further example, we may note how early in the day the inhabitants of Scotland set an example in this matter. I quote from Havelock Ellis, who being always at least fifty years ahead, was not discerned by the crowd behind, and indeed they hardly caught a word he said. Thus we might with advantage hear a few words now. 'Through superfluity of cleverness and wickedness — however admirable each of these qualities may be in

moderation — Man has involuntarily entered into a contest with Nature, fatal alike to him and to her, yet a
contest from which it is hard to draw back. Its fatality
for Nature we see at every hand. As regards one small
corner of the world, Dr. James Ritchie, who speaks with
authority, has lately drawn a terrible picture in his substantial work on *The Influence of Man on Animal Life in
Scotland*. Man arrived late in Scotland — he had
already touched the Neolithic stage — and he found rich
fauna there on his arrival. He proceeded to destroy
utterly the nobler fauna of free and beautiful creatures —
many of them working for his good had he but known —
and replaced it by a degraded fauna, virtually of his own
creation, and yet only existing to prey upon him. He
found the reindeer and the elk and the wolf and the
brown bear and the lynx and the beaver and the otter
and the buzzard and the bittern and the water-ousel and
the golden eagle and the sea eagle and the osprey and
the great auk. And he killed them all. And in their
stead he placed by countless millions the rabbit and the
sparrow and the earthworm and the caterpillar and the
rat and the cockroach and the bug, scarcely or at all
found there before he brought them, and they have
flourished and preyed. For, as Ritchie has shown, Man's
influences upon Nature, even when it seems but tiny and
temporary, is yet in its total effect greater than imagination can grasp.'[1] And Havelock Ellis adds that in result
today we see man everywhere surrounded by a cloud of
animal and vegetable parasitic vermin, from rodents to
bacteria, multiplying at such a rate that he cannot overcome them, while they prey upon him and slay him and
make him so generally poisonous that when a boatload
of Europeans is landed on a remote island inhabited by

[1] *Impressions and Comments*, 3rd series. Sorry he includes the earthworm!

simple natural men it has sometimes left death-spreading infection behind.

While it may fairly be said that we in the Old World are thorough enough in these crimes and follies, the Americans are justified in feeling that there is room for improvement in the rate of destruction. They displayed some progress in this. On reaching the great plains they found the buffaloes. Through the tall and deeply rooted grasses with their seas of flowers in spring, these animals moved in herds ten thousand strong. The trampling of their hooves could be sensed from a long way off by the trembling of the earth, while the bellowing from their throats at the mating season could sustain a comparison with thunder. Numbered by the million, there was yet pasturage for them all as they migrated through the plains and wandered by the streams and roamed over the mountains, leaving broad paths and even splendid thoroughfares in their wake. They were many; but it did not take more than a century for the whites to press them back to the wall of the Rocky Mountains and there slay them for sport, leaving their carcasses to rot on the plain after their tongues had first been cut out to provide a tasty dish for the epicures in the towns. Following the buffaloes, came the deer, the elk, the moose, and the bear to supply further targets for the rifles of the sportsmen. 'On high peaks,' says Mr. Stuart Chase in a lovely image, 'were mountain goats and mountain sheep clinging with airy grace to the edges of eternity.' They also were fair game and good sport. The fun gathered speed. The sporting champions came into their own. One man claimed to have slain in a single year one hundred and thirty-nine thousand birds and animals, while another countered with the disposal of seven thousand ducks in a season, though both

were considered inferior to the prowess of the Chesa-
peake hunters who with swivel guns killed one thousand
five hundred ducks in eight hours for a New York market.
Soon the sound of wild life grew faint. A silence fell upon
the land. The wind-like swish of the wings of the
passenger pigeons whose flight had once darkened the
skies for days on end as they passed over Kentucky, was
stilled, and their bodies were thrown to the pigs. The
beaver built his dams no more — he had been turned
into hats. The fish could no longer live in the many
lakes, rivers, and brooks which had been turned into
sewers. The call of millions of water-fowl was not heard
again when marshes were drained for unnecessary crop-
lands. By the present century it was reported that nine
species of bird and ten species of mammal were entirely
extinct, while twenty-five species of bird and twenty-six
species of mammal were threatened.

And the wild horses who had poured over the plains
in droves? Not one roams now, even within the memory
of living men. Are they then lost to us, and shall they
never more be seen? Ah no, we see them still; they yet
print their proud hooves on the receiving sod before our
very eyes — for have they not been sung by America's
own mighty Melville? 'Most famous in our Western
annals and Indian traditions is that of the White Steed
of the Prairies; a magnificent milk-white charger, large-
eyed, small-headed, bluff-chested, and with the dignity
of a thousand monarchs in his lofty overscorning carriage.
He was the elected Xerxes of vast herds of wild horses,
whose pastures in those days were only fenced by the
Rocky Mountains and the Alleghanies. At their flaming
head he westward trooped it like that chosen star which
every evening leads on the hosts of light. The flashing
cascade of his mane, the curving comet of his tail,

invested him with housings more resplendent than gold
or silver-beaters could have furnished him. A most
imperial and archangelical apparition of that unfallen
Western world, which to the eyes of the old trappers and
hunters revived the glories of those primeval times when
Adam walked majestic as a god, bluff-browed and fear-
less as this mighty steed. Whether marching amid his
aides and marshals in the van of countless cohorts that
endlessly streamed it over the plains, like an Ohio; or
whether with his circumambient subjects browsing all
around at the horizon, the White Steed gallopingly
reviewed them with warm nostrils reddening through
his cool milkiness; in whatever aspect he presented himself, always to the bravest Indians he was the object of
trembling reverence and awe.'[1]

In place of the wild life that had held the natural
equilibrium, entered the employed animals, the cattle
and the sheep. The grass and the bison had thrived
together, but the hooves of the steers in excessive quantity punished the prairie, and the paths became gullies,
while at the same time the sheep, cutting into the very
heart of the grass, killed acres of it outright. Indeed, so
unpopular did the sheep become in the eyes of the cattle-
men that the latter fought the sheep-men, call them
not shepherds, until sometimes on a dark night there
would be the slaughter of twelve thousand sheep. This
was the true background to the romance of the cowboys
of the Wild West from the Potomac to the hills of Kentucky, from Ohio to the reaches of the Mississippi, and
the long rolling verdures of the prairies and the plains.
The cowboys were but the tough hirelings of the Beef
Barons whose business grew to such dimensions that
thirty million dollars of Scotch and English capital were

[1] *Moby Dick.*

eventually involved in it. For we must never forget that the British policy of 'cheap food' was a main cause in the destruction of American soil.

## § V   ANCIENT VERSUS MODERN IDEA OF NATURE

WE have come a long way, as I have already observed, from the conception of trees as gods. A very long way indeed. It is not a happy contrast. Could we draw back and regard these operations of our forefathers in America, with the eye, not of a human being but of an animal involved in the invasion, they would offer a fearful spectacle. Since we cannot do this we can at least try and see it as from a high place. For many centuries the land had remained under the equilibrium of the Natural Order. Suddenly it was broken in upon by a race of men from across the sea. And with what violence, with what hatred against all living things! There had never been anything like this before in the history of man and nature. There had been many civilizations. Men had grown up with nature in this place and that place. They had seldom been wise or good in their relations with earth. They had made many mistakes, huge blunders in tree-killing, soil-injury, and water-wastage for which they had been repaid with dust and sand. But there had never been anything like this that occurred, and occurs, in modern days under the sign of mechanism. When we think of the ripping up of the grass in every direction, of the crashing down of huge trees under the axe and the deliberately lit forest fires rushing forward at the rate of an express train while thousands of animals shriekingly fled in terror from the crackling flames till exhausted they were burnt alive, our minds and our hearts turn back to the primal days of religion and reverence. For what had those beauty-blind mechanical destroyers, those reality-scared lumber-jacks, to do with any sort of religion? Do they not seem only as large insects, or as a plague of locusts eating every-thing before them without the excuse of being driven blindfold in the coils of necessity? We think back, I say, we turn our hearts again to the days when man was un-clouded by his comforts and uncorrupted by his engines. We think of the origin of ploughing and the first mystery of milk, of the meaning of the cow and the mourning at harvest.

Consider the ancient fields. Men hardly dared touch them. The first plough, made of gold and drawn by sacred animals, was used only as a ritual in the temple gardens to do homage to the god of fertility. Even so, that scratching of the soil was regarded as a kind of *wounding*, a sacrifice of earth for the good of her children. The plough was considered so sacred that the fugitive who reached it found protection as certainly as the thief who stole it suffered retribution. The idea of being torn — or ploughed — was linked with the mystery of genera-tion, and the Indian earth-mother Prithivi, having first surrendered herself in the form of a cow to Prithu, could only become fruitful when her lap was torn as with a plough. This symbolism was also recognized by the Athenians who legally sealed wedlock upon the imple-ment; and the ancient Irish, embracing in one mighty image the starry heavens and the fruitful earth, first spoke of the constellation of 'The Plough'.

Thus also with oxen. The origin of oxen as partners with man was equally rooted in ritual. The sacred bulls that first drew the holy chariot in the procession of the temples were so sacrosanct that the killing of an ox was an act of murder punishable with death; and even after the annual ox-sacrifice at the Athenian rite of Bouphonia, the presiding priest was compelled to fly from the country and to throw his bloody axe into the sea.

Thus also with milk. It was unthinkable as nourishment and conceived only in the light of a ceremonial drink, and so treated by the Orphic and Dionysian priests that it induced a kind of spiritual intoxication, its deathless properties being symbolized by the Egyptians in many a mysterious rite. Thus we see representations of the goddess Nuit in the form of a cow suckling the King to bestow upon him the gift of eternal youth; and just as in Egyptian wall-painting the plough is the tool in the hand of Osiris, so we can read on their tomb-inscriptions 'Isis giveth thee milk', or 'The Cow Hesah giveth thee milk'. In what lay its virtue? Do we know and can we tell that mystery? — or are we far too much enfolded within layer on layer of crusted knowledge that divides us from the pristine impact on an unscored mind? Perhaps it had something to do with its *whiteness* — the colour that in all ages has served as the symbol of divine spotlessness and power. Certainly we may say that if the ancient nobility of Scotland were washed with milk, and the Picts of Ireland used it as a salve against poisoned arrows; if Romulus poured out a libation of milk at the founding of Rome, and the Todas of India laid their dead on a bier in the milk-chamber; if the milk of human kindness was numbered by the early Christians as the greatest of all virtues, and a never-empty pitcher of milk was lifted to the lips of the martyrs; if to the still sensitive souls of men there is no loftier sign than the Milky Way, we must conclude that here we have a real feeling for the profundities of existence not unmixed with dread at offending the demands of deity.

This approach to the Creation did not last. The day

came when the ceremonies fell into disrepute and a 'practical' application was made to the ritualistic object. Then the plough could become a tool. The ox could become a carrier of burdens. Milk could become nourishment. A rent was torn in the mind of man and we entered the era of economics. In order that milk might become food the symbolism had to be forgotten. 'In effect the spiritual world had to be denied', says Dr. Pfeiffer. 'What a mighty fall of humanity took place when the holy emblem of deathlessness, of the passing of the threshold at birth and death, became mere nutriment.'[1] Is this the real Fall of Man, or at least for us today, the Fall that means most? Is it this that creates the unease which shadows us always as we walk in the harsh light of modernity?

When we remember these early conceptions regarding the earth, and the wounding of the earth, and the sacred oxen and the ritualistic milk, and then turn to the Beef Barons and the Ploughmen Kings and the Timber Magnates of America, it is hard to equate them with progress. Wounding the earth! — with what axe could one open the skull of a modern lumberjack on the spot or lumber merchant off the spot, and plant that idea therein? It is totally beyond the conception of the big tough guy with the tiny mind. Think of the modern harvest with its hundredweight sacks fetching so many dollars or shillings, as against the gathering and the garnering in the ancient days amidst weeping and voices raised in mourning songs! They felt guilty for what they had done. They had robbed the earth, their mother. They had taken without giving. They must show contrition and entreat forgiveness. Amidst the lamentations of the populace an image of the goddess, Demeter, in the form

[1] See *The Earth's Face*, chap. 9, to which the present writer is deeply indebted.

of a mighty grape, must be carried in triumph and then dismembered as a symbol of the bleeding vine; and just as the primitive African apologized to a tree he had cut down or injured, so must the disciple of Manes at the harvesting of grain entreat the presiding deity: 'Not I have harvested thee, nor have I finely ground thee, nor do I place thee in the oven. Another accomplished this deed. Guiltless I ate it.'

Such feelings were widely experienced. From the Sagas of the north to the Mysteries of the south, from the ballads that celebrated the torment of John Barleycorn to the mourning maidens of Islam who at the baking of bread bewailed the passion of the god, Tamuz, we see in many forms and under many signs the expression of guilt, the lamentation for death, and the belief in resurrection. It was not until these ideas faded that the harvest could become an occasion for gaiety, festival, and riotous rejoicings. Such scenes would have appeared as shocking to the primitive ploughman as our gross commercialism of Christmas would seem to the early Christian. Today there is neither weeping nor rejoicing. We are not sorry, and we are not glad. We have no time, for we must keep pace with the machines. Even the gracious ceremony of grace before meals has been abandoned; for that would seem too much like thanking Tom Campbell for ploughing his nine million acres for which he has already received his pieces of silver. We owe debts to no one. We have nothing to fear.

## § VI AGAIN THE TREES REPLY

OR have we? Until recently we did not think so, and the Americans certainly did not think so. But now nature has made her reply and shown her hand. Let us watch what happened in the North American continent — or, rather, some of what happened in some places, for as I have said before, I am concerned in this book to make a statement, not to give an exhaustive survey.[1]

Let us proceed with caution. I am anxious to avoid exaggeration in this matter. There is no need for rhetorical tropes. Every American was not then and is not now a villainous despoiler of nature. Furthermore, if we permit our minds to move freely in contemplation of earthly phenomena, human and otherwise, we cannot fail to recognize that the planting in a few years of a civilization on that mighty virgin land, is one of the marvels of history. The sowers sowed the seeds of cities, roads, railways, machines, factories, men (up to 150 million). It may be that they will not last longer than flowers, and will sink back into the spent and unconsidered earth. But how prodigious the effort, and how magnificent the show. When we approach Manhattan from the ocean and see those towers rising from the water to assault the clouds; and when later we walk through the canyons of New York confusing top-storey lights with stars, we cannot but acclaim the lyric splendour of that stage. It may not be permanent, and the scene-shifter behind may be compelled to remove it or its inhabitants; but that will not lessen the brief glory of the play.

At the moment that civilization is still holding up large portions of Europe as well as itself. Let us see just what it has to stand upon now. In 1630 the land offered 820 million acres of forest, 600 acres of grassland, and 430 million acres of open woodland. Today it is calculated that not more than one-tenth of the forest remains and

[1] For the alarming story of South America, see VOGT's *Road to Survival*.

that the annual loss exceeds the annual growth by over fifty per cent; and it is calculated with regard to the soil that one-half of the fertility of the continent has been dissipated. That is to say that though there has been great loss of soil there is still a great acreage remaining. For we must recognize that a continent of that size whose soil has been built up through millennia cannot be utterly destroyed for some time, however enlightened and progressively mechanical the attackers may be. Nevertheless what has happened is sufficiently impressive.

The first thing, as we have seen, was the attack on the trees. They came down. They were very valuable when alive and standing, for, again as I have shown in proper place, they were grips, they were stakes, they were sponges — the twigs, leaves, rotting logs, pebbles, and stones at their feet serving as a filter and retarder of floods. They were mowed down and the ground was ploughed — that is loosened — where they had stood. That is the first thing. Then the tiny trees came down. I mean the grasses, for in relation to the soil they might be called little trees, as they also keep it in place by their root-grips and wind-cushioning stems. They also were attacked, mown down and ripped up by speedy mechanical means, and prairie fires were lit that rivalled the conflagrations of the woods. Those were the two main movements in the subduing of the wilderness.

And they were the two main causes in the erosions that followed. At the very moment when the pegs were taken up the carpet was cut into pieces. It was exposed to wind which first having dried it could then blow it away. At other places, exposed to unchecked torrents of rain, it could be washed away. The details concerning this have been rehearsed over and over again by all the experts on the subject, and therefore brevity here on my part is surely desirable. We need but to remember a few salient facts. Nitrogen, phosphorus, potassium, and sulphur are four of the most important ingredients in the soil. In a virgin land they have been built into it through centuries of undisturbed give and take in the diurnal round. They are so light and insubstantial as to be defenceless if exposed to wind or flood. Thus bare ground turned by the plough can lose as much fertility in ten years as unbroken prairie in four thousand years (which also forms even as it goes). Consider the irreplacable network of filter and sieve which we call roots. Remove them and the result is that water simply messes up the clay and the sun bakes it into chunks which are shifted into the valley by the next shower if the land is on a slope — while the unpercolating water rushes as from a roof, carving a gully in its passage. On a steep field a pouring thunderstorm will let loose up to four hundred tons of water per acre per hour — all of which could be successfully channelled if cushioned by trees. Without resistance four hundred tons of water can make itself felt and leave its mark. A piece of land in Georgia which was forested and calculated as having lasted for 35 thousand years, was uncovered and showed signs of disappearing in 25 years.

Consider also the effect of vast monocultures over wide expanses of cropland — of course those minerals were used up whether they were blown away and washed away or not. They went out over the railways into the cities and across the seas. It is so easy to forget that we eat the soil. We in Europe have eaten a great deal of American soil. They have recklessly shipped it across to us. It has been sent in the form of wheat or beef — the latter having first over-grazed and hoofed the soil it fed on.

Once more, think of the inheritance of the new people

in the new world. They came to two billion acres, half in forest; forty per cent in strong grasses; only two per cent in desert. From the Atlantic to well beyond the Mississippi stretched unbroken primeval forest. That was the wealth they took over, the deposit they found in the earthly bank. They broke into the chest and rifled its contents, calling their action 'sturdy individualism' or 'ameliorative improvements', or simply 'the enterprise of capitalism'. What is the opposite to that kind of capitalism? It is not socialism. It is not communism. It is conservatism. The opposite to capitalism is conservatism. But up till this century the idea of conserving anything never entered the American mind. The fantastic towers of the speediest growth in history rested upon the swift plundering of nature's hoarded wealth. That was the foundation upon which they built their house. Was it built on sand? And is it writ in water?

At first the reckoning was not easy to discern. Good yields were naturally expected and achieved at the beginning — it was a long time before a depreciation of *fifty per cent* was discovered! It is not easy for farmers to discern the least spectacular but most deadly form of soil wastage, namely sheet-erosion — the invisible washing away of the surface good stuff in high places into the valleys and the rivers. The farmers above who began to lose in their yields did not know what was happening any more than the farmers below who became richer by virtue of the unexpected deposit. The latter began to wake up and to become less pleased when later on the offering they received from above was in the form of useless under-soil and then of pebbles and stones.

That was sheet-erosion, to be found wherever the land sloped — and eighty per cent of America is sloping. But manufactured erosion is dynamic and cumulative. It grows by what it feeds on. In the civilization of speed it was itself speedy. At last the Americans began to look round with alarm. They had taken over the soil. But it would not stay still, it was not a stable thing. They had cut down the trees. They could not cut down the wind, they could not control the rain. The accumulation of twenty thousand years of soil-building was failing before their eyes — in a single century thousands of years of fertility was being thrown away. There is a belief that we live by the soil. There is a general idea that we live on mother earth, and since there is plenty of earth, all is well. The trouble is we only live on the *top* of the earth, we have only the *top* of the soil to play with — a spade's depth. Thus are we perched precariously. If that surface goes we go with it. That surface began to go rapidly in America, as elsewhere, and men to go with it.

After the sheet, followed the gully erosion. Small gullies carved by torrents unarrested by any obstacle were so deepened and widened that in some places spectacles of astonishing bleakness and devastation were created. Canyons had literally been carved in less than a century over hundreds of acres which previously had shown neither gully, nor ravine, nor canyon. That was bad enough, but the increasingly uncontrolled nature of the rivers was more immediately catastrophic. Living by the banks of a great river began to become more dangerous than living under the shadow of a volcano. Some of the towns that had been built upon the banks of the Mississippi were no longer safe, and at a moment's notice could be and often were submerged in flood or totally swept away. Yet this loss to human life and property was nothing compared with the continual day by day loss of soil carried to the sea. The Mississippi alone carried — and still carries — 400 million tons of solid earth to the Gulf of Mexico, taking with it the microscopic organisms that make humus what it is — the minerals amounting to 40 million tons of phosphorus, potassium, nitrogen, and sulphur. Already by 1936 it was calculated that 100 million acres of formerly cultivated land had been essentially ruined by water erosion, which is an area equal to Illinois and Ohio, North Carolina and Maryland combined; it was further calcuated that the washing of sloping fields elsewhere accounted for the stripping of the greater part of the top-soil over another 125 million acres; and that further, calculating from approximately ten years ago, another 100 million are on the way out — which gives a total of over 300 million acres likely to be confined to the dust-heap.

It will not amuse any American to speak figuratively of dust-heaps. For that brings us to the worst form of erosion. The carriage of the soil to the sea by water is not greater than carriage by air. The Great Plains were opened to the winds, and the wind has been carrying them away ever since. This form of erosion, taken with the action of water as above, brings the figure up to three billion tons of top-soil lost every year. A storm of dust on May 11th, 1934, meant that 300 million tons of fertile soil was swept off the great wheat plains and carried to places where it was utterly useless. It meant the laying down of sand dunes and the creation of landscapes that look (in photographs) as if an enormous snowstorm had covered up all but the tops of houses, trees, and ravines. Everyone knows that the now famous Dust Bowl which takes in portions of Oklahoma and Kansas, Colorado and Texas and Wyoming, blows its farms two thousand miles away into the Atlantic Ocean.

These storms do not dispose of more soil than is

accomplished through the agency of water, but by all accounts they are unspeakably vile. To die of 'dust pneumonia' in that once clear-lit land upon which nature smiled with bountiful promise, must be a terribly unpoetical end. To see your farm submerged in dust, as has happened, must promote feelings far more drab than those of the Etna peasant whose farm may disappear, not owing to man's folly, but to the fiery nature of the earthly depths. In the year 1935, in a derelict and wasted farm between Wyoming and Texas, the corpse of a man was discovered in the sand. What had happened to him we wonder? Had he been ill and unable to escape? What secret lay buried in his tomb of dust? And what did the dying eyes behold? A height had loomed up behind him. A mountain? — ah no, it was not a solid: no crags were there, nor crooked cliffs upon which the eye could rest serenely. It was not a liquid: it had no vapour in it that might let fall rain to drench his parched and wasting land. It was the soil itself that had got up there. It was America blowing away. 'Behold my country!' he may have cried. 'Behold our dreams, our hopes, our plans and works, our triumphs and our spoils — now turned to dust!' And perhaps in those last lonely hours he may have fully felt the awful folly and the vast rebuke.

§ VII THE REFUGEES FROM THE WRATH
THAT CAME

THE scenes of dereliction were not confined to abandoned fields and prairies turned to dust. The ravages of the revenge were not marked only by hideous gaps and gullied scars on land where once the trees had stood. We see another scene as well — the spectacle of deserted houses, deteriorating farms, and a horde of hungry, wasted, angry men.

Remember the philosophy of the men of speed. The land is inexhaustible: get what you can here, there is more beyond. It was a sort of mining above ground. They would rush at a place, cut down all the trees, set up a great lumber industry, build a town, and promote a thriving agriculture in the clear spaces. Then one day they would begin to find that there were no more trees left in that area, and that the soil was not suitable for concentrated agriculture after all! The mills would fall silent — the mills that had ground so exceeding fast. This led in many cases to the abandonment of whole towns and even of whole counties.

Thus they arrived in the Jackson County of the Lake Superior region. The lumber men assailed the white pine. The trees fell down. Mills, railroads, stores, houses took their place, and the region boomed. Then the farmers moved in to share the prosperity. The pine having been annihilated and exchanged for the pleasing spectacle of stump, scrub, and brush, the ex-timber workers cleared more land for farms, and put into operation big drainage schemes. It turned out to be too sandy. There was complete failure for farmers on the spot. But in the cities behind, it all provided a speculator's holiday. They began to promise fortunes out there to unsuspecting townsmen. 'Come to Jackson County and make your Fortune in its Rich Irrigated Loams.' The suckers sucked. They came, they saw, they failed, they starved. The whole county went into bankruptcy, and streams of *refugees* trailed across the land at the mercy of the successful, strong settlers who had gone ahead and captured further land. These were the grapes of wrath; these were the men fleeing from the wrath that had come in the wake of folly and greed. And there were many of them, multitudes three thousand strong swarming on the highways. They had come out to exploit the land and had been exploited by the first exploiters. They would gladly have defaced the earth for cash, but others had got in before them, and nothing now could be reaped as nothing sown save a crop of infamy. Hating and hated, bitter and violent, these the foolish ones turned their beauty-blind eyes with devouring greediness upon the possessions of the wise, and as they flowed through California, wave upon wave of them, hungry and homeless, and onwards further west through Kansas and Oklahoma, Texas and New Mexico, Nevada and Arkansas, they presented a spectacle of defeat and shame, of misery and degradation such as we associate with the refugees displaced by the wars of man with man. In this case the spectacle was one episode in man's conquest of nature — when the conquered were the conquerors.

It may be urged, of course, that we must not take the plight of these people too seriously. They represent a mere three hundred thousand out of one hundred and fifty million. A sad chapter, but not important. It is over now. It cannot happen again since all the land is plotted out . . . Yet is it over? Is the hour of famine, is the sight of refugees fleeing from the wrath of outraged nature, a thing of the past? Voices are still raised in warning that deserts in America, *equal to the size of the Sahara*, must follow the depletion of soil which nature can only replace at the rate of an inch every five hundred to a thousand years. It is said that in forty years there will be no reserves of timber; and there are not lacking authorities, authoritative or otherwise, to declare that in a hundred years there will be no food resources left. For myself I have far too much faith in man's respect for his own skin, and in the present conservation schemes, to think that it will come to this. But it is also perfectly obvious that before America comes to terms with nature — if she ever does — we will see a great deal more punishment exacted in unyielding soil and rotting men.

When I think of these things, my mind goes back to certain scenes in an Englishman's book. The author was a man of transcendent genius, whose ability to present atmosphere, amongst other things, was so great that his works are read in every portion of the world where books are known. Near the end of the nineteenth century he paid a visit to America, and when he came back he wrote *Martin Chuzzlewit* — in which he sent his hero to that country. When I read the book for the first time I was puzzled by the account of Martin's dinner with Mr. Jefferson Brick and others. A bell rang. Instantly the gentlemen who were walking with him dashed up some steps into a street door like lunatics. Evidently it was an alarm bell and the premises were on fire. While Martin was looking for the smoke, more of the company, with horror and agitation depicted on their faces, came plunging wildly round the street corner, and all together threw themselves in at the same door. Entering to see what was up, Martin 'was thrust aside, and passed, by two more gentlemen, stark mad, as it appeared, with fierce excitement'. When Martin was in the room he could see no fire, but only a dining-room in which a meal had just been served. 'It was a numerous company,' says Dickens, 'eighteen or twenty perhaps. Of these some five or six were ladies, who sat wedged together in a little phalanx by themselves. All the knives and forks were working away at a rate that was quite alarming; very few words were spoken; and everybody seemed to eat his utmost in self-defence, as if a famine were expected to set in before breakfast time tomorrow morning, and it had become high time to assert the first law of nature. The poultry, which may perhaps be considered to have formed the staple of the entertainment — for there was a turkey at the top, a pair of ducks at the bottom, and two fowls in the middle — disappeared as if every bird had the use of its wings, and had flown in desperation down a human throat. The oysters, stewed and pickled, leaped from their capacious reservoirs, and slid by scores into the mouths of the assembly. The sharpest pickles vanished, whole cucumbers at once, like sugar-plums, and no man winked his eye. Great heaps of indigestible matter melted away as ice before the sun. It was a solemn and an awful thing to see. Dyspeptic individuals bolted their food in wedges; feeding not themselves but broods of nightmares, who were continually standing at livery within them. Spare men, with lank and rigid cheeks, came out unsatisfied from the destruction of heavy dishes, and gazed with watchful eyes upon the pastry. What Mrs. Pawkins felt each day at dinner time is hidden from all human knowledge. But she had one comfort. It was very soon over.'

Why were they so hungry? I wondered when I first read that description. Why were they so continuously hungry, according to Mrs. Pawkins, 'as if a famine were expected to set in before breakfast'. The passage has the force of unconscious symbolism or prophecy. Reading it today it seems like a picture in miniature, either of the manner in which Americans were busy devouring their continent, or of men frantically feeding before the hour, close at hand, when there would be nothing left to eat. It is strange that Dickens, a nineteenth-century Londoner, who knew less about forestry and soil erosion and cared no more about them than Bill Sikes himself, should have made a fable here. But then Dickens was Dickens, who had that enormous capacity for sensing the essential in an atmosphere. When I took up *Martin Chuzzlewit* for the first time, I remember looking forward to reading his famous attack on America — scenes, I supposed, of Dickensian humour playing upon American foibles in the land of boundless promise and prosperity, as it then seemed. But no such thing. That was not the impression — or not chiefly. The main impression left in the reader's mind is the ironically named Eden where Martin and Mark Tapley go to seek their fortune — a ghastly place in the wilderness, a petrified forest, a swampy sink of fever. The easy victim of some speculators, Martin went to just such a place as thousands of other optimistic land-greedy men arrived at in those days, full of hope which quickly changed to despair.

Those two main impressions made in the mind of a reader of the American part of *Martin Chuzzlewit* are the very last things which one would expect Dickens to hold up at the end of the nineteenth century in the land of apparently boundless activity, opportunity, and properity. Yet such are the pictures that the great man did hold up — famished diners, and 'cities' of dereliction and dismay.

The Americans had declared war on nature, and had come away with many spoils and triumphs. Then nature declared war on them; already by 1936 when *red snow* fell in New England, it could be calculated that the dust offensive and the water offensive had taken away one-half of the original fertility of the continent; and in 1948 we are assured by the Soil Association that its annual loss of production soil by erosion is 3,000,000000,000 tons — enough to fill a train of freight cars girdling the earth 18 times, and the equivalent of 73,000 forty-acre farms washed or blown away.

The trees had fallen. Nine-tenths of the trees had fallen from all that mighty host. They were dead, and since their carcasses are much more useful than dead men, they were marvellously transformed into a thousand implements. But suddenly it was found that they were even more useful when alive. They were the only police force that could protect man himself from the ravages of tempest and of flood. God was, after all, on the side of the green battalions, and man must retreat before the mockery of this Moscow.

# BIBLIOGRAPHY

ZON, R., *Forests and Water*

SEARS, PAUL, *Deserts on the March*

CHASE, STUART, *Rich Land, Poor Land*

PFEIFFER, EHRENFRIED, *The Earth's Face*

JACKS, G. V. and WHYTE, R. O., *The Rape of the Earth*

PERSON, H. S., *Little Waters*

BAKER, RICHARD ST. BARBE, *Green Glory*

GARDINER, ROLF, *England Herself*

PEATTIE, DONALD CULROSS, *The Road of a Naturalist*

MASSINGHAM, H. J., *The Tree of Life*

VOGT, WILLIAM, *The Road to Survival*

OSBORN, FAIRFIELD, *Our Plundered Planet*

BARLOW, K. E., *The Discipline of Peace*

SYKES, FRIEND, *Humus and the Farmer*

FAULKNER, E. H., *Ploughman's Folly*

MCWILLIAMS, CAREY, *Ill Fares the Land*

TOYNBEE, A. J., *A Study of History*

HUXLEY, ALDOUS, *Beyond the Mexique Bay*

JEFFRIES, RICHARD, *The Wood From the Trees*

RADIN, PAUL, *The Story of the American Indian*

CATLIN, G., *The American Indians*

STEIGER, G. N., *A History of the Far East*

SKRINE, F. H., *The Heart of Asia*

MALLORY, W. H., *China: Land of Famine*

TAYLOR, W. L., *Forest and Forestry*

ROWE, W. H., *Our Forests*

EVELYN, JOHN, *Sylva*

KINGDON-WARD, F., *About This Earth*

RADCLIFFE, F., *Flying Fox and Drifting Sand*

# PART FIVE

# CONCLUSION

# CONCLUSION

MAN is a dramatic animal. He leans towards tragedy. He courts disaster. Born finally to obey or perish, he must first defy the laws of earth and usurp the throne of God.

We have followed something of this drama. We cannot pursue it to the end on paper, for the last Act has not yet been played. The climax may have been reached but not the dénouement. There is another Act to go. Since we are the players, what happens depends on us.

When trees were regarded as gods they were not cut down. Hence the mountains also stayed up, and the soil remained steady, and the waters true. When trees came to be regarded simply as 'timber' they were ruthlessly slain. We have rehearsed some of nature's replies with the swollen river and the plague of rodents, with the day of drought and the bowl of dust.

Yet there is this to be said about man. He learns from history. History is experience. When we put our hands in the fire, we learn never to do that again. If the experience is painful we learn and we act. Already the Americans have learnt. They are taking steps. Having nearly destroyed themselves by their exertions they may save Europe by their present example. They are soil-erosion conscious as no nation has ever been before. They know what has happened. They know what they ought to do. They have experienced a sufficient amount of calamity to make them act. Man must have calamity, he must have disaster, before he can save himself. The Americans saw the floods rise, and the dust blow, and the

237

earth melt from beneath their feet. When such things happen men become sincere. For today, as at all times, the human animal, nearly shipwrecked, will turn towards some means to save itself. The ideas of the shipwrecked are the only genuine ideas, said Ortega Y. Gasset: all the rest is rhetoric, posturing, farce. The shipwrecked man 'will look round for something to which to cling, and that tragic, ruthless glance, absolutely sincere, because it is a question of his salvation, will cause him to bring order into the chaos of his life'.[1] The Americans heard the cries of the shipwrecked — and they have acted. The whole world has heard of the Tennessee Valley Authority. What they did there, what they are doing elsewhere in the replanting of their forests and the conservation of their soil, may save them from total disaster and eclipse.

The story of man and trees in Western Europe has not been so calamitous in result as the American. Nevertheless nearly a thousand years war was declared against trees in Western Europe. It is not the fault of the deforesters that the land is not now in worse shape than it is — the fact is of course that the invaders of the American continent had the conditions for a real rape of the earth, not hitherto available. The European situation with regard to deforestation is too complicated to be subject to a general statement. But it is only too obvious that today, the Scandinavians, who have largely kept their trees, are in a very much better position with regard to fertility than Southern Europe, especially Spain whose once tree-covered country is now a scene of almost Eastern poverty. Again, the Germans are world famous for their forests and their foresters. Today the trees are falling fast under the axe of the occupying

[1] *The Revolt of the Masses.*

238

powers. But let us remember that it was the Nazis who first set about exploiting German and Austrian forests without any regenerative policy whatever. They wished to use their trees as weapons of war, and did so with such thoroughness that by 1942 it could be written: 'Clad in fabrics produced from wood, living on wood sugar, wood proteins, and meat and cheese from wood-fed cattle, with a schnapps ration made from "grain" alcohol obtained from sawdust, German soldiers move to the Russian battle lines in wood-gas-driven trucks, which are greased with tree-stump lubricants and run on Buna tyres made from wood alcohol. Spreading misery and destruction with explosives manufactured from the waste liquors of woodpulp mills, they are assisted in their nefarious work by squadrons of plywood planes, while the German propaganda division takes a motion-picture record of selected items of the action on a film made of wood cellulose acetate.'[1]

The trees have had their revenge all right. And, one way or another, it will return on us, we may be sure, if we further deface the German forests.

In England forests once covered nearly the whole land. Envoys returned to Caesar saying that they could not penetrate to the end of them. In due course they also were cut down. There has been much re-growth since, and reckless cutting of the re-growths, but still many woods remain to the tree-loving British, while of course a supply of rainfall has never been a problem for the islanders.

For my part, I think that the danger to England caused by the primary destruction of her forests, goes very deep. The nemesis is very real and very terrible. It goes underground. Already by the fifteenth century so many

---

[1] 'The Rediscovery of Wood' – *American Forests*, September 1942.

forests had been cut down that wood as fuel was beginning to become scarce. When Aeneas Sylvius, later
Pope Pius II, paid a visit to England in 1458 he noted
in his diary how pleased the poor people were when they
were given stones for alms. 'Nam pauperes pene nudos
ad templa mendicantes,' he wrote, 'acceptis papidibus
eleemosynae gratia datis, lactos abusse conspeximus; id
genus lapidis, sive sulphurea, sive alia pingui materia
praeditum, pro ligno quo regio nuda est, comburitur' —
the sense of which would read: 'Now we have seen begging
at the temples, poor people almost naked: who, when
they had been given stones for alms, went away happy.
That kind of rock, which may contain sulphur or some
other rich material, is burned instead of firewood when
the district is bare.' That is to say already coal had
been discovered, and that branch of forestry which we call
coal-mining, had begun. First we cut down the forests
standing above ground. When they were exhausted
there remained the woods underground — the carboniferous forests. Coal mining is a branch of forestry and
agriculture: but we dig deeper, we cut without planting,
we reap where we have not sown.

Thus that great day came when the carboniferous
forests were located and the properties of coal were
realized. Perhaps this was the most exciting discovery of
all. We are weary of such things now. Our hearts are
cold and cowed. But we shall be lacking in imagination
if we cannot realize what it must have seemed like in
those days, the excitement which the words of George
Stephenson must have held for all who heard them:
'We are living in an age when the pent-up rays of that
sun which shone upon the great Carboniferous Forests
of past ages, are being liberated to set in motion our mills
and factories, to carry us with great rapidity over the

earth's surface, and to propel our fleets, regardless of wind and tide with unerring regularity over the ocean.'

We must allow a certain epic grandeur in their theme. The power was divined. The wealth was realized. The possibilities seemed boundless. Naturally there was a coal rush. Claims were staked out by the enterprising and adventurous, and messengers were sent down into the primitive forests. A strange journey indeed! Strange wanderings in those sunken lands! Pioneering down into the darkness, the travellers explored that green old world of long ago. They made perpendicular roads and descended as far as three miles into the buried woods. They carved out galleries within them. They ran trucks through tunnels chiselled from the petrified leavings of the rotten reeds. And as they passed along those corridors encased by the corrupted ferns, and penetrated ever further into the lost regions of the sunlit lands, the danger from gases obliged them to go in darkness with nothing to lighten their way save the phosphorescent gleam from dried fish.[1]

They encountered more perils than explosive gases. In making their way through the subterranean forests they sometimes came upon tree-trunks standing erect, the interior being sandstone and the bark converted into coal, so that as soon as the stance of such trees was weakened they often suddenly fell, killing the men below. 'It is strange to reflect', says Sir Charles Lyell, 'how many thousands of these trees fell originally in their native forests, in obedience to the law of gravity, and how the few which continued to stand erect, obeying, after myriads of ages, the same force, are cast down to immolate their human victims.' But nothing daunts the spirit of man. In heaving out these precious rocks, this bottled

---

[1] Until the 'Davy Lamp' was invented.

energy, for expansion in the upper world, no effort was too much, no sacrifice in flesh and tears too great, and hundreds, even thousands of these visitors to the ancient woods gave up their lives and lay down eternally entombed amidst the sepulchres of the trees.

This enterprise was pursued with such zeal and concentrated industry that during the nineteenth century England cut out more of these forests, this coal, than was cut out elsewhere over the *whole world*. This changed England utterly. Her history was altered. She was forced to enter on a road all unforeseen. It caused the colossal industrialism of the country. That is by far the most important effect which trees have had upon England. They had been sleeping below. They were disturbed. When they were carried to the surface they were in the form of great potential activity. Once they had got to work they changed everything, including characters and faces. As for their effect upon population, a twenty million increase is an underestimation. Thus England became one of the most powerful countries in the world. Then the most vulnerable. And now?

Everyone knows her dilemma now. No country in the world, or in history, has ever been less ecologically sound than the England of today with its population of fifty million, ninety per cent of whom work at non-agricultural activities caused by the carboniferous forests. That is the fact. When food fails presently to come in from other countries how will the fifty millions get on? The question is enough to make a tree laugh. This ever hanging threat is the cause of the gloom which has fallen upon the English of late — they feel they have no *footing* on earth.

The realization that things had taken a dangerous course was expressed in the phrase 'back to the land'. But it was soon laughed out of court as pleasing romanticism. The British decided to ignore this gigantic threat. The clear-eyed prophecies of woe carried through from Cobbett to Carlyle and from Ruskin to Morris were stifled by the Fabians who, suddenly and calmly *accepted industrialism*. Their influence in this was enormous. From then onwards the political sociologist could speak solely in terms of the *rights* of man instead of his *needs*, and of his welfare instead of his responsibility to earth if he is to exist at all. A whole generation came under that influence. The only thing necessary, it was said, is good distribution: distribute as many things as possible to as many people as possible and all will be well — that was the concern of economics. And even when at last Laments for Economics were raised, and the Death of Economic Man announced, there was not the faintest attempt from that quarter to make way for the arrival of Ecological Man. It was a world of plenty, we were told, and the crime was poverty in the midst of plenty — and soon, so very soon, we were to find that the opposite was the truth, and that all we can hope to see, as demonstrated by black markets, is plenty in the midst of poverty.

Under the same influence the educationalists went on and on and on declaring that what was necessary was more schools and better buildings and more teachers, while they continued to allow generation after generation of school children to grow up with the idea that manual work is degrading, that muck-heaps are dirty, that harvesting is something to do 'on your holidays', and that it is more dignified to be a nonentity in a town than a solid workman in the fields upon whom the whole world depends — the contemptible fatuity of which ideas can only be really felt by someone who knows both worlds. I will add this only here — that those ideas are not only contemptible, they strike against the psychological and physiological needs of many millions of children later doomed to a life of nonsense which they are forced to accept. And on the intellectual side, is it worth pausing to inquire before closing this paragraph, to what extent Ecology is taught?

The more influential of the *literati* took the same industrial line. The man to be respected was the workman in the towns. The middle-class intelligentsia suddenly found enormous merit in being an industrial worker. As for love of nature, or appreciation of her laws, that was regarded as outmoded and sentimental. Instead of examining the ground upon which they stood, they gazed steadily at the Horizon. Instead of seeing the mud in the Yellow River, they dreamed of the Moon in the Yellow River. It was a conspicuously urban poet residing in London who led a generation to turn their attention from the waste land of the soil to the private Waste Land of the soul. It was he who declared that 'April is the cruellest month'. It was all very well for one great man in one bad mood to say that once. But it was not a good thing when a whole generation took this as the proper response to nature . . . And yet, industrialism had reached such a pitch that perhaps it was inevitable, and there was at least sincerity in that response. It is said that in France and in Central Europe during the last two centuries, fifty per cent of the philosophers and poets stemmed from mountainous regions. Perhaps it was natural that at a time when England had reached a culmination of industrialism and was busy ruining her farmers, April should have appeared the cruellest month to a generation of metropolitan poets whose sole connection with agriculture was confined to the sowing of a little wild oats, and who had never climbed a mountain higher than Parliament Hill.

It seems to me that the time has come for Advanced Guards — philosophic, educational, poetic, scientific — to cohere for once and make their countrymen conscious of the ecological situation. It is a comprehensive theme. 'We have learned to see in mythology', says Dr. Pfeiffer, 'a good deal of physiology and natural scientific wisdom.' In this book I have tried to bring together the intuitions of the past with the factual knowledge of the present. We have reached a time when we can get our bearings. We can discard superstition without replacing it with irreverence. We can sense the invisibilities on a higher plane of apprehension. Edward Carpenter said that he once managed to glimpse at any rate a partial vision of a tree. 'It was a beech, standing somewhat isolated, and still leafless in quite early Spring. Suddenly I was aware of its skyward-reaching arms and upturned finger-tips, as if some vivid life (or electricity) was streaming through them into the spaces of heaven, and of its roots plunged in the earth and drawing the same energies from below. The day was quite still and there was no movement in the branches, but in that moment the tree was no longer a separate or separable organism, but a vast being ramifying far into space, sharing and uniting the life of Earth and Sky, and full of a most amazing activity.'[1]

We cannot all reach these visionary heights, nor can any man remain there. But we can all be ecologists. There are in England today agriculturalists with astonishing practical genius combined with comprehensive ecological insight. Trust England to produce such men! If they are supported and allowed to lead the way and show the means towards the greatest compromise England has ever been called upon to make, the compromise between industry and agriculture, then

[1] *Pagan and Christian Creeds.*

England could regain her balance. But she must make up her mind about it. The English can do anything if they make up their minds upon a course of action — but they do not like doing so, they would rather drift. Can we afford to drift any longer? If the present unecological life is continued and other countries are relied upon to support us — why, then that cutting down of the forests which led to the cutting out of the squashed and hoarded wealth of wood below, will have meant disaster. For trees always have the last word.

Rather we should say, more broadly — nature always has the last word. And having said that, should we not be glad? The issue may sometimes be physically painful, but it is at all times metaphysically inspiring. We can never really wish that we were in charge of the scheme and responsible for it, since we are perfectly aware that we understand very little of the works and nothing of the springs. It would be the darkest pessimism to suppose that *we* could have the last word — for it would be bound to spell disaster. We can do a great deal to upset the equilibrium, but the balance will always be eventually restored — at our expense. If we realize that we *could* work in with that equilibrium and be upheld in the arms of nature, then we cannot fail to experience the motions of courage and hope.

# INDEX

# INDEX

# INDEX

# INDEX

# INDEX

# INDEX

# INDEX